HIGH OCTANE

The Fastest Motor Racing Series in the World

MELVYN RECORD

HIGH OCTANE

The Fastest Motor Racing Series in the World

MELVYN RECORD

THE
APPLE
PRESS

A QUINTET BOOK

Published by The Apple Press
6 Blundell Street
London N7 9BH

ISBN 1-85076-568-5

This book was designed and produced
by Quintet Publishing Limited
6 Blundell Street
London N7 9BH

Creative Director: Richard Dewing
Designer: Peter Laws
Project Editor: Claire Tennant-Scull
Editor: Lydia Darbyshire

All photographs © Kay Presto at Presto
Productions except: p.12, PPG Industries,
p.16, Australian FAI IndyCar Grand Prix
(© Murray Waite & Associates), p.17,
Phoenix International Raceway, p.18, Penske
Speedways Inc., p.19, Molson Indy
Vancouver (photographer, Robert Kwong),
p.20, IMG Detroit Grand Grand Prix (© Mick
Kuskowski, photographer), p.21, Elkhart
Lake's Road America Inc., p.66 & 67, Indy
500 Photos (© Ron McQueeney,
photographer), p.73, Toyota Motorsports,
p.85, Indy Regency Racing Inc.
(photographer, Cheryl Day Anderson)

Typeset in Great Britain by
Central Southern Typesetters, Eastbourne
Manufactured in Hong Kong by
Regent Publishing Services Ltd.
Printed in China by
Leefung Asco Printers Ltd.

CONTENTS

Originally known as American Automobile Association (AAA) championship racing, IndyCar racing has come a long way in its near-90-year history.

Although historians will argue over when the AAA series officially began, some say 1902, others 1909 and 1916, there is no disputing that IndyCar racing is the longest continually-scheduled motor sport championship series in the world.

The first AAA national champion was British. Driving a Peugeot, Dario Resta won the title in 1916 in a series of races at Indianapolis Motor Speedway (IMS) and at board tracks, (so called because of the pine board surface). Resta won the IMS race after 300 miles, the only time in the event's history that the race was scheduled for anything less than 500 miles.

IMS opened in 1909, with the original race surface made of crushed rock and tar. The first 500-mile race took place two years later by which time the surface had been replaced with more than 3 million paving bricks (hence the nickname, "The Brickyard"). Ray Harroun won that first race in six hours, 42 minutes, with an average speed of just 74.5 mph.

After World War II the racing series continued to represent a meeting of two very different disciplines of motor sport. The series' jewel in the crown, the Indianapolis 500, was contested on a paved oval and the remainder of the races that made up the AAA national championship were contested on dirt ovals which had replaced the maintenance-intensive board tracks around the country. This change meant that the drivers had to be skilled in both forms of racing and by the mid-1950s race teams were building and campaigning two distinctly different cars: one specifically for the paved ovals, the other for dirt tracks.

'IMS OPENED IN 1909, WITH THE ORIGINAL SURFACE MADE OF **CRUSHED ROCK** AND TAR'

The difference in the two types of race cars ultimately led to the national series abandoning championship races at dirt tracks. The cost of building and maintaining two different race cars had become prohibitive and such races were removed from the schedule in 1971.

At the conclusion of the 1955 race season AAA stopped sanctioning races and the United States Auto Club (USAC) was created and charged with administering the series, which had at last begun to include more paved ovals on its schedule.

USAC continued to guide the

'FOR SHEER WHEEL-TO-WHEEL **EXCITEMENT** THERE IS LITTLE TO COMPARE NEXT TO 200mph INDY CARS'

sport until November 25, 1978. The team owners became disillusioned with the way that USAC had been handling the development of the sport and created a new entity: Championship Auto Racing Teams, Inc., or CART for short. Early goals for the fledgling organization included responding to competitors' needs; courting potential sponsors and catering for existing ones; the promotion of the events themselves; and educating the media and the public about the sport.

Although any organization that is administered by its participants is often a recipe for disaster, CART not only succeeded in reaching its early goals, it positively flourished, to the extent that today IndyCar racing is perhaps second only to Formula 1 in terms of global reach and popularity.

Nigel Mansell's arrival in IndyCar racing at the beginning of 1993 turned the attention of the motorsports community toward North America's premier open-wheel series and let the outside world know what millions of Americans were already aware of: that for sheer wheel-to-wheel excitement there is little to compare next to 200-mph Indy cars.

INTRODUCTION

ndyCar is one of those rare organizations in which the participants make the rules. It's been compared to the inmates running the prison, and the 24-man board of directors regularly take plenty of criticism for the situation from the North American motor racing media.

Some of the criticism stems from perceptions of how the IndyCar board has furthered the aims of the original "breakaway" team owners who formed CART in 1978. The car owners decided they knew how to promote the sport better than the USAC could,

and, for the most part, they have been proved correct.

However, for all the glamorous (and not so glamorous) race tracks at which the IndyCar series competes during a season, the jewel in the crown is the Indianapolis 500, and that race remains a USAC-sanctioned event. In 1991, Tony George, the president of Indianapolis Motor Speedway, put a proposal to the IndyCar board that would have put the sport under one roof. The proposal was rejected but, in a compromise move, George was offered the position of a non-

ABOVE **There are many power brokers in IndyCar racing, but perhaps none is more powerful than Tony George (right), the president of Indianapolis Motor Speedway.**

voting member on the IndyCar board in 1992.

In 1993 George agreed to stage a National Association of Stock Car Racing (NASCAR) race at the Speedway in 1994. For years, Indy cars have raced in the shadow of the full-bodied stock cars, which consistently draw more spectators at tracks where the two series race. Despite reservations from IndyCar racing's biggest supporters that the NASCAR race would not be popular with fans who were more used to watching open-

wheel race cars at the track, ticket demand for the inaugural Brickyard 400 more than doubled that for the Indy 500.

When former IndyCar president and chief executive officer William Stokan resigned, the IndyCar board announced it would seek to replace him with a racing man. Tony George's close friend Cary Agajanian was a racing man if ever there was one – his father J. C. Agajanian operated the legendary Ascot Park in Los Angeles and owned a fleet of Indy cars in the 1950s and 1960s – but

ABOVE **The Indy 500 attracts the largest crowd for any single-day sports event. Almost 500,000 fans cram into the Indiana course on race day.**

he failed to secure the position. Instead, Andrew Craig, a marketing man from Britain, was appointed, and George quit the board, announcing plans to organize a second IndyCar series, starting in 1996, that would include the Indy 500.

THE MAN IN CHARGE

'FOR YEARS, INDYCARS HAVE RACED IN THE SHADOW OF FULL-BODIED STOCK CARS'

Andrew Craig happily acknowledges he has no talent as a racing driver: his brief motor racing career being restricted to a 1-litre Chevron Formula 3 car in the early 1970s and a Sports 2000 entry in the late 1980s. Despite this, Craig has been charged with steering IndyCar into the 21st century.

Craig's background is primarily in marketing. Before taking up his position as president and chief executive officer of IndyCar, Craig was deputy chief executive at International Sports & Leisure, a Swiss-based company that has done marketing work for the International Olympic Committee and the World Cup. International Sports & Leisure acquired the marketing rights for the Olympic Games in 1985 – an area in which Craig specialized – and substantially increased sponsorship for the Games – something the Board of Directors hopes Craig can do for IndyCar.

LEFT **Andrew Craig was appointed chief executive officer of IndyCar on 7 January 1994. Craig, an Englishman, has been given the responsibility of guiding IndyCar racing into the next century.**

PPG INDUSTRIES

ABOVE **Carol Wilkins is PPG's Manager, Communications and Motorsports. 1994 marks PPG's 15th consecutive year as the main sponsor of the IndyCar World Series.**

In an area of sport dominated by tobacco companies and their sponsorships, IndyCar racing stands alone in having a unique, non-tobacco benefactor: PPG Industries.

Founded in 1884 as the Pittsburgh Plate Glass Company, it changed its name to PPG Industries in 1969 to reflect its diversification and global expansion. It is now one of the world's largest manufacturers of flat glass and continuous-strand fibreglass and has almost 50 production facilities in North America and 90 more scattered around the globe.

However, for motor racing fans, PPG is better known for its involvement in North America's premier open-wheel racing series: IndyCar. PPG Industries sponsored its first Indy car event in 1979, posting $25,000 in prize money for a 150 mile USAC race at Trenton Speedway in New Jersey. Satisfied with its first involvement in the sport, PPG Industries announced its sponsorship of the entire series later that same year. In 1994 PPG Industries paid $1 million to the series champion.

In 1989 PPG expanded its involvement in the series to include Indy Lights, which is considered the development programme for future IndyCar drivers and teams.

'INDYCAR RACING STANDS ALONE IN HAVING A UNIQUE, **NON-TOBACCO** BENEFACTOR'

ABOVE **PPG's name has become synonymous with IndyCar racing. Although it is an extremely diverse company, it is probably best known to motor sport fans for its automotive coatings.**

IT'S A SMALL WORLD SERIES AFTER ALL

Although it is officially called the PPG IndyCar World Series, the title somewhat overstates the championship's true global reach in terms of competition, for it currently takes in rounds in only three countries: North America, Canada and Australia. The name does, however, accurately reflect the series' international make-up in terms of participating drivers and its outstanding foreign television coverage.

There can be no question but that, for what is essentially a North American racing series, it does attract a cosmopolitan range of drivers, with 14 different countries represented in the series in 1994.

In addition to Australia and Canada, five other countries have hosted rounds of the IndyCar series since the mid-1950s: Italy (1957 and 1958), Japan (1966), Argentina (1971), Britain (1978) and Mexico (1980).

TELEVISION

These days, the success of any sport, be it soccer, cricket, or, in this case, motor racing, is judged on how much television exposure it can generate. IndyCar racing is one of three major North American motor sports that has its entire series televised on network and cable television (the other two are NASCAR stock cars and NHRA drag racing).

All IndyCar races are televised in North America, on either the ABC network or the all-sports cable network ESPN. In fact, it is claimed that in 1994 the IndyCar series got more network television than all other motor sports combined, and through ESPN International, viewers in more than a hundred countries worldwide are able to watch some of the greatest racing drivers battle it out across North America.

However, of all the races televised, one stands head and shoulders above the rest as the most watched: the Indy 500. In 1993 the race gained an impressive 8.5 television rating (one rating point is equal to 942,000 households in North

'IN 1994 THE INDYCAR SERIES GOT **MORE** NETWORK TELEVISION THAN ALL THE OTHER MOTOR SPORTS COMBINED'

RIGHT **Television plays an important part in all sports. Motor racing has been made more exciting for armchair enthusiasts by the introduction of on-board cameras, seen here on the left of the rollbar.**

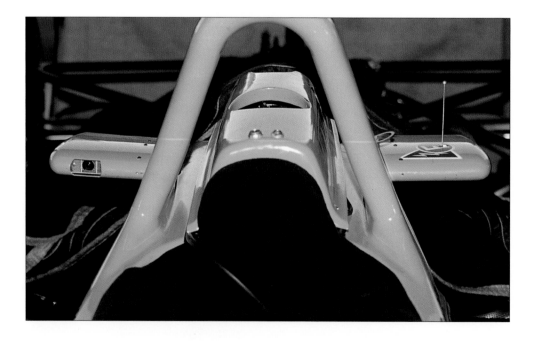

ABOVE **To give viewers a bird's-eye view of the races, cameras are mounted on scaffolding. This one is placed near the start/finish line at Phoenix International Raceway.**

ABOVE **ESPN's Gary Gerould interviews Indy Lights driver Greg Moore. Constant television attention helps viewers to become better acquainted with the sport's stars.**

America) on the ABC network, and the qualifying sessions that precede the race itself are also broadcast on ABC and ESPN.

In April 1994 president and chief executive officer Andrew Craig sold all IndyCar's television rights to ESPN for five years, beginning 1995. The multi-year agreement calls for all IndyCar races to be televised live, with a minimum of half the series broadcast on ABC, and the remainder being shown on ESPN. The agreement provides for a guaranteed minimum payment to IndyCar, a revenue-sharing plan, and permission to release race-event and television schedules in advance.

RACE TRACKS

Homestead Race Circuit
Miami, Florida
permanent road course, new to Indy Car tour for 1995

Surfers Paradise
Queensland, Australia
2.7-mile, 16-turn temporary road course

Phoenix International Raceway
Phoenix, Arizona
1-mile oval course

Long Beach
Long Beach, California
1.5-mile, nine-turn temporary road course

Indianapolis Motor Speedway
Speedway, Indiana
2.5-mile oval course

The Milwaukee Mile
West Allis, Wisconsin
1-mile oval course

The Raceway on Belle Isle Park
Detroit, Michigan
2.1-mile, 14-turn temporary road surface

Portland International Raceway
Portland, Oregon
1.9-mile, nine-turn permanent road course.

Burke Lakefront Airport
Cleveland, Ohio
2.3-mile, 10-turn temporary road surface

Exhibition Place
Toronto, Canada
1.7-mile, 11-turn temporary road course

Michigan International Speedway
Brooklyn, Michigan
2-mile oval course

Mid-Ohio Sports Car Course
Lexington, Ohio
2.2-mile, 13-turn permanent road course

New Hampshire International Speedway
Loudon, N. Hampshire
1-mile oval course

Pacific Place
Vancouver, Canada
1.6-mile, nine-turn temporary road course

Road America
Elkhart Lake, Wisconsin
4-mile, 11-turn permanent road course

Nazareth Speedway
Nazareth, Pennsylvania
1-mile tri-oval course

Laguna Seca Raceway
Monterey, California
2.2-mile, 11-turn permanent course

SURFERS PARADISE, AUSTRALIA

One of five street race courses on the IndyCar tour, the event is held in downtown Surfers Paradise, Brisbane, and marks the only stop on the 16-race series where a race is held outside continental North America. Michael Andretti, debuting the new Reynard chassis, won the 1994 race, while Nigel Mansell set a new one-lap track record of 106.05 mph in claiming the pole position around the 16-turn, 2.79-mile temporary course.

LEFT **The surf-side track at Surfers Paradise, Brisbane.**

ABOVE **A bird's-eye view of Phoenix International Raceway.**

PHOENIX INTERNATIONAL RACEWAY

After opening the season south of the equator, the Indy cars return to North America and to Phoenix International Raceway in Arizona. The tight one-mile oval provides plenty of excitement, with the 1994 version including a huge crash involving Canadians Paul Tracy and rookie Jacques Villeneuve. Fortunately, neither driver was hurt. Prior to his spill, Tracy had set a new record in qualifying at 176.26 mph in his Marlboro Penske entry, and team-mate Emerson Fittipaldi took an ultimately comfortable victory.

MICHIGAN INTERNATIONAL SPEEDWAY

The fastest track on the schedule, Michigan International Speedway, located in Brooklyn, Michigan, is a high-banked two-mile oval where only the brave, and sometimes the lucky, do well. Nigel Mansell, driving the Newman-Haas Lola, qualified on the pole position with a 233.73 mph lap for the 1994 event but was out of the running after 35 laps with a broken throttle

ABOVE **The two mile oval of the Michigan International Speedway.**

linkage. First Raul Boesel, and then Al Unser Jr, appeared set to win until they, too, succumbed to mechanical problems, allowing Canadian Scott Goodyear victory in his Kenny Bernstein-owned Lola. Mansell's team-mate, Mario Andretti, holds the track record at 234.27 mph, set in 1993.

THE MILWAUKEE MILE

Held one week after Indy, the Milwaukee Mile allows drivers to get back into their racing routine after one month of qualifying, testing, and racing at Indianapolis. The comparatively flat (only 9-degrees of banking in the turns) one-mile oval means the cars are not as fast as at some other oval courses, but quick none the less. After dominating the Indy 500 with their Mercedes-engined Penskes, the trio of Al Unser Jr, Emerson Fittipaldi, and Paul Tracy reverted back to their more familiar Ilmore powerplants and scored the first of five 1–2–3 finishes at the 1994 race. Nigel Mansell again had the quickest car in qualifying, setting the pole position with a 158.22-mph lap, but could not match the pace of the Penskes.

PACIFIC PLACE VANCOUVER

Of the five street-course events on the IndyCars tour, two take place in Canada, the latter of the two being at Pacific Place in downtown Vancouver, British Columbia. The 1.67-mile, nine-turn temporary road course puts a premium on driver skill, and for a while during the 1994 race it appeared as though Robby Gordon, driving the Valvoline Lola, would score his first career victory. However, Al Unser Jr snatched the lead after two-thirds distance and won the race. Unser's victory effectively clinched the 1994 IndyCar Championship.

LEFT **The crowds at the Pacific Place street course in Vancouver.**

THE RACEWAY ON BELLE ISLE PARK

The Detroit Grand Prix isn't actually held in Detroit, it's held on Belle Isle, a stone's throw away from the motor city, hence the name. On this twisty, 14-turn, 2.1-mile course, Nigel Mansell again proved his race car prowess in 1994 by setting a new

ABOVE **The picturesque Belle Isle Park Raceway.**

track record of 108.64 mph to claim the pole position and, indeed, led the first lap. But after this the Penske cars took over and Paul Tracy claimed the win ahead of team-mate Emerson Fittipaldi.

NAZARETH SPEEDWAY

The penultimate stop on the 1994 tour, Roger Penske's trio of drivers are very much at home at Nazareth Speedway, located in the beautiful mid-East Pennsylvania countryside. Owned by Penske, the track is a one-mile tri-oval (so called because of its slightly triangular shape). In qualifying for the 1994 event Emerson Fittipaldi smashed the track record with a 185.6-mph lap (the previous record being

ABOVE **Nazareth Speedway in the heart of Pennsylvania.**

181.43 mph by Michael Andretti set in 1992), and the Marlboro Penske drivers netted their fifth 1-2-3 finish of the year, with Paul Tracy heading Al Unser Jr, and Fittipaldi across the finish line. So dominant were the Penske cars, they finished four laps ahead of fourth-placed Raul Boesel.

ROAD AMERICA

The longest course on the schedule, Road America, situated in Elkhart Lake, Wisconsin, is a sweeping 11-turn, four-mile permanent road course favoured by many drivers. The 1994 race provided one of the season's few genuine surprises when rookie Jacques Villeneuve outmanoeuvred Paul Tracy and Al Unser Jr on a restart and held on to take a dramatic victory. Prior to the 34th-lap restart, Paul Tracy, the pole sitter with a 136.80-mph lap, had held the lead from the beginning of the race but ultimately finished 18th, the result of a broken engine.

ABOVE **The grand sweep of Road America.**

TRACK RECORDS

Most consecutive laps led: 198 by Billy Arnold in 1930

Most laps led by a non-winning driver: 196 by Ralph DePalma in 1912

Greatest number of lead changes: 29 by five drivers in 1960

Greatest number of drivers to lead race: 10 in 1980

First official 4-lap 200-mph qualifying speed:
202.156 mph (325.269 kph) by Tom Senva in 1978

First official 1-lap 200-mph qualifying speed:
200.535 mph (322.66 kph) by Tom Senva in 1977

COMPETITION RULES

Like all sports, the only way to ensure some semblance of fair competition is through the enforcement of rules, and IndyCar is no exception.

ABOVE **Of paramount concern to the sport's administrators is driver safety. All the cars are built with a crash-resistant tub that helps protect the driver in the event of accidents.**

CONSTRUCTION AND SAFETY REGULATIONS

LEFT **Officials use computerized equipment to check the dimensions of race cars to make sure they meet IndyCar specifications.**

'OF COURSE SOME TEAMS ARE BETTER AT INTERPRETING THE RULES THAN OTHERS'

All cars competing on the IndyCar tour must comply with specific construction and safety rules. The purpose of the rules is both to ensure maximum safety for the drivers while they are in the vehicles and at the same time to impose the same standards on all the participating teams. Of course, some are better at interpreting the rules than others.

For races held in 1994, all Indy cars must be between 190 and 195 inches (4.95-4.82 m) long, and they must have a minimum wheelbase of 96 inches (2.44 m), measured between the centre line of the front and rear wheels. The previous wheelbase was between 109 and 112 inches (2.77-2.84 m). The highest point of the car must be no more than 32 inches (81 cm) above the ground, excluding the roll-over hoop located just behind the driver's head and the rear wings on short oval and road courses, where a maximum height of 36 inches (91 cm) is allowed.

Two distinct types of engine are permitted: turbocharged four-stroke, overhead cam, eight-cylinder, with a maximum capacity of 2,650 cc (161.7 cubic inches); and turbocharged production-derived (more commonly known as a stock block), single non-overhead cam with pushrod-operated valves, with a maximum capacity of 3,403 cc (209.3 cubic inches).

All the cars use methanol fuel (as opposed to petrol, which is used in Formula One racing), and they must be capable of achieving at least 1.8 miles (2.9 km) per US gallon (3.785 litres). The maximum fuel capacity for each car is 40 US gallons (151.4 litres), and the fuel is contained in a ballistic rubber bladder, located behind the driver but in front of the engine.

The whole package rides on 14 inch (35.5 cm) wide (maximum) rear wheels and 10 inch (25 cm) wide (maximum) front wheels, and it must cross the scales weighing 1,550 pounds (703 kg), including coolants and oils.

QUALIFYING

efore a driver can start an IndyCar race, he or she must first qualify for the race field. Indy cars race on two different types of race track – ovals and road courses – and there are, therefore, two different qualifying procedures, one for each course.

At the oval courses the drivers make two flying laps around the track, with the quicker of the two being the one that determines where a driver will start the race.

ABOVE **The sequence of qualifying attempts for oval tracks is determined by a draw.**

On the road courses each driver is given two "sessions" in which to record his fastest lap, although unlike on the oval tracks, where there is only one car on the track for each qualifying attempt, the driver not only has to race against the clock but must also dodge the other cars that are trying to qualify. After two qualifying sessions the driver's quickest single lap determines where he or she will start the race.

Just making the starting grid for the Indy 500 is an achievement in itself. The 500-mile race regularly attracts more than 50 drivers and teams attempting to make the field, so being one of the 33 participating teams on Memorial Day weekend (the end of May) is something to write home about.

However, the process by which drivers qualify for the event is somewhat complicated, particularly for the first-time visitor to the Speedway. The 33 drivers qualify for the event during two weekends of time trials held before the race itself. The starting positions are not determined on a best, or quickest, single lap, as in Formula 1, but rather on the average of four consecutive circuits of the 2½-mile race track. The starting grid is further complicated because position is determined by what day a particular driver recorded his or her net average speed.

What all this means is that the first few rows of the starting grid are determined on the first day of qualifying, but hypothetically it is possible for the fastest car in the field to start the race at the rear of the grid if the driver happened to have a bad day (mechanical breakage or similar) during the first day of qualifying.

Each driver is given three attempts in a particular race car to qualify for the race. If a driver chooses to stop or is forced to stop before the completion of the fourth qualifying lap, he or she has two more chances. Should the car in which the driver is attempting to qualify prove not fast enough, he or she may use another car that has not yet qualified and get another three shots at making the field.

Once 33 cars have qualified for the race, a process known as "bumping" – something more commonly associated with drag racing – begins. A driver who is able to exceed the speed of the 33rd qualifier, theoretically the slowest car on the grid, bumps out that particular driver and joins the grid.

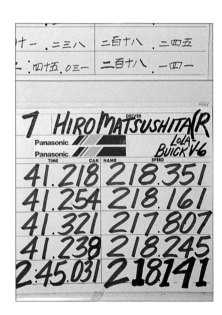

‘THE DRIVER MUST ALSO **DODGE THE OTHER CARS** THAT ARE TRYING TO QUALIFY’

ABOVE **Although winning the Indy 500 is, of course, the high spot of the annual Memorial Day weekend race, simply qualifying for the event is cause for celebration.**

RACING CONDITIONS

One element that can greatly affect the outcome of any given race is the weather, particularly wet weather. Because of the nature of racing on ovals, the race does not begin if the track is wet. Only when the racing surface is dry will the cars begin to make their way to the track.

Road races, however, are different, and wet weather often proves to be a great equalizer of competition. Brute horsepower doesn't always win the day, and driver skills become a more important factor.

In wet weather, the chief steward may declare the beginning of the race either as a "dry start" or a "wet start". If he deems the race is a "dry start", the drivers have the option of beginning the race on either dry-weather tyres (more commonly known as slick because of their lack of tread patterns), or wet-weather tyres (with tread patterns). If the chief steward determines that the beginning of

LEFT **Motor racing tyres are being continually developed and improved. Nigel Mansell tried this set of tyres at Phoenix International Raceway before they were sent back to Goodyear for further analysis.**

'BRUTE **HORSEPOWER** DOESN'T ALWAYS WIN THE DAY'

the race is a "wet start", all participating drivers must begin the race on wet-weather tyres.

The race is officially finished when the lead car has completed the scheduled distance and/or the chequered flag has been shown. In the unlikely event that one of the participating teams feels there has been some violation of the rules by another team, it has 30 minutes in which to protest at the results, which must be done in writing and with a $500 (£350) protest fee.

INDYCAR SAFETY TEAM

LEFT **Safety Team vehicles are positioned around the race courses to retrieve disabled vehicles so that they do not endanger other drivers.**

ABOVE **One of the best known of safety personnel within motor sports is Dr Terry Trammell, director of medical services for the Safety Team medical staff.**

When driver A. J. Foyt was seriously injured in a pit fire at the 1981 Michigan 500, Carl Horton knew the time had arrived for IndyCar racing to develop the resources to establish its own safety team, a group of dedicated people, experienced in everything from fire fighting and driver extraction to major trauma, on whom the drivers knew they could count at every race to help them out of potentially life-threatening situations.

Horton's dream was realized in 1984 when the Safety Team made its debut, and it provides safety, rescue, and medical services for IndyCar racing. Since its creation, the Safety Team has grown to meet the ever-increasing needs of driver safety, expanding in terms of both equipment and personnel. A squad of 23 staff have access to six specially equipped vehicles.

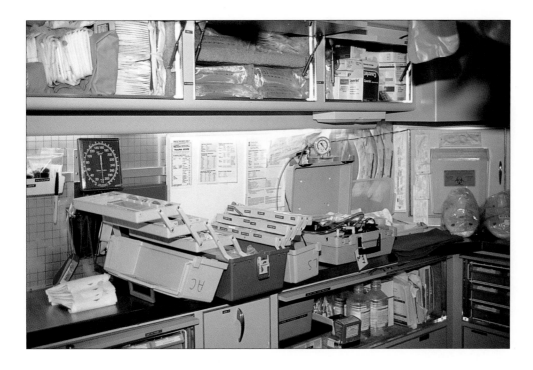

LEFT **The mobile medical centre is equipped to handle almost every kind of injury, and it includes a pulseoximeter, a cardiac monitor and a defibrillator for cardiac arrest. Computer records of each driver's previous injuries and prescribed medication are also kept.**

'THE SAFETY TEAM HAS GROWN TO MEET THE **EVER-INCREASING** NEEDS OF DRIVER SAFETY'

The centrepiece of the Safety Team's vehicles is a converted coach, which serves as a mobile trauma centre, capable of treating several people at any one time. Standard equipment in the coach includes oxygen, heart monitor and defibrillator, high-frequency ventilator, X-ray, orthopaedic capabilities, stretchers and a pharmacy. An on-board computer gives doctors instant access to the medical records of the participating drivers.

Supplementing the mobile trauma centre are two GMC crew cabs, which act as emergency response vehicles on track in the event of an accident. Each truck is staffed by a physician, paramedic, and a minimum of two people who are experienced in rescue and extraction techniques. Additionally, each truck carries firefighting, medical and rescue equipment.

During the 1993 racing season the medical staff treated more than 500 people with ailments ranging from sore throats to major trauma.

CHAPTER TWO

INDYCAR-
NUTS AND BOLTS

ABOVE **The Penske, which is constructed in Britain at Poole, Dorset, was the leading chassis through 1994. Here, Emerson Fittipaldi puts his Ilmor-engined car through its paces at Phoenix International Raceway.**

29

CHASSIS

There are three chassis manufacturers in IndyCar racing: Penske, Lola and from 1994, Reynard. Somewhat surprisingly for what is essentially a North American sport, all the chassis are built in Britain.

PENSKE

The Penskes are built in Poole, Dorset, in a factory that was originally built for Roger Penske's brief involvement with Formula 1. The first Penske chassis victory came in 1978, when Rick Mears drove to victory at the Milwaukee 150, and since then (until the 1993 race season), another 72 winners' trophies have been added to the trophy cabinet. Unquestionably, the best season for the Penske chassis came in 1979, when it carried Mears, Bobby Unser and Gordon Johncock to 10 straight victories.

Although many teams would like to use the Penske chassis, it is not available to everyone. The chassis are built exclusively for Roger Penske's team, and usually the only way to get one is when the Penske team has finished with a chassis, and it is sold second-hand.

LOLA

The dominant car builder in modern IndyCar racing is Lola, which is based in Huntingdon, near Cambridge. Eric Broadley, the man behind the Lola name, first raced his brand of cars in the late 1950s, mostly in British sports car and Formula Junior events. Lola's first Indy victory came in 1966, when Graham Hill won the Indy 500 in a Lola T90.

Lola began selling its Indy car chassis in 1984 and, although it does not have an "official" factory team, the Newman-Haas outfit is almost an "unofficial"

ABOVE **The Lola chassis is one of the more adaptable in IndyCar racing. Built in Britain, the chassis can accept Ford, Ilmor and Honda engines.**

'SOMEWHAT **SURPRISINGLY** FOR WHAT IS ESSENTIALLY A NORTH AMERICAN SPORT, ALL THE CHASSIS ARE BUILT IN BRITAIN.'

LEFT **The Reynard chassis had a spectacular introduction to IndyCar racing, winning its first race in Australia. Here, Teo Fabi puts his Reynard through its paces on the one-mile oval at Phoenix International Raceway.**

RIGHT **After exhaustive tests, Reynard have established the definitive 941 shape.**

team. Other significant teams using the Lola chassis in 1994 include Derrick Walker Motorsports and Budweiser King Racing.

The Lola T94 chassis was designed by John Travis and Keith Knott. It is very adaptable, being able to accept Ford-Cosworth, Ilmor or Honda engines. Improvements to the 1993 model that were made for 1994 included better weight distribution, suspension geometry, a transverse transmission, improved air flow around the headers, a carbonfibre monocoque and a lower front nose.

Throughout the early 1990s Lola was the chassis to beat, despite the best efforts of Penske. Between 1990 and 1993 Lola chassis won 44 of a possible 65 races and claimed the PPG IndyCar series title with four different drivers: Al Unser Jr (1990), Michael Andretti (1991), Bobby Rahal (1992) and Nigel Mansell (1993).

REYNARD

Adrian Reynard's chassis manufacturing outfit had an impressive record to live up to when it entered IndyCar competition at the beginning of 1994. Since making its debut in international races in Formula 3 in 1985, the Reynard chassis had won all its debut races, regardless of category.

Driving a Reynard 94I, designed by Malcolm Oastler and built at the manufacturer's plants in Bicester, Oxford, and Brackley, Northampton, Michael Andretti kept the company's staggering record intact by winning the Surfers Paradise race in Brisbane, Queensland, Australia.

ENGINES

There are currently three engines of choice in IndyCar racing: Ford-Cosworth, Ilmor and Honda. For the Indy 500, which is a USAC-sanctioned event (and therefore not subject to IndyCar rules), two other engines are also used: the recently introduced Mercedes-Benz and the Menard (formerly known as Buick).

IndyCar rules restrict all engines to a maximum of eight cylinders, and they can be of the stock block variety or purpose built for racing.

Stock block engines have pushrods (as opposed to overhead camshafts) to operate the valves and can have a maximum cubic capacity of 3,430 cc (209.3 cubic inches). Overhead cam engines, which are purpose built for racing, are allowed a maximum capacity of 2,650 cc (161.7 cubic inches).

Both kinds of engine are

'THE NEW MERCEDES-BENZ ENGINE IS ESTIMATED TO DELIVER A **STAGGERING** 900 HORSEPOWER'

allowed turbochargers, which use engine exhaust gases to spin a turbine, which in turn powers a compressor that forces more air into the engine's intake system. Because turbocharger pressures can vary, the manifold is equipped with a pressure relief valve – a "pop-off" valve, as it is known in racing circles. If the turbocharger pressure exceeds 45 inches (114 cm) of mercury – 50 inches (127 cm) on stock block

engines – the pressure is vented. Although the system is hated by most participating teams, it does ensure some semblance of fair competition and stops one team from running more turbocharger boost pressure than another.

Horsepower figures, actual and estimated, are a closely guarded secret in IndyCar racing, but educated guesses range between 700 and 850 horsepower, depending on turbocharger setting. The new Mercedes-Benz engine, which was used for the first time at the 1994 Indy 500, is estimated to deliver a staggering 900 horsepower.

In an effort to try to peg costs for engines and to stop one engine supplier from dominating the sport, as tends to happen in Formula 1, IndyCar rules dictate that manufacturers that are new to the series must offer their engines to a minimum of three

cars in two teams in their first year of competition, and to six cars in three teams in their second year of competition. The key word here is offer. No team has to take the engine, but it must be offered. The price of the new engine is set by IndyCar, and it is based on the aggregate of different engine suppliers from the previous year, with a maximum cost increase of 10 per cent.

Between 1988 and 1993 Chevrolet tended to dominate, to such an extent that in 1990 and 1991 the only cars to win any races were running Chevrolet engines. Ford-Cosworth, which had been the dominant engine supplier until the mid-1980s, returned to IndyCar racing in 1992, and since then the two manufacturers have more or less split the victories, although Chevrolet maintained a two-to-

ABOVE **Engines come in a variety of packages, but perhaps the most exotic was the Porsche unit, which made its first appearance in 1987. The engine never lived up to its potential, however, and Porsche eventually withdrew from the sport.**

one advantage throughout the 1993 season.

Chevrolet's involvement in IndyCar racing came through its 25 per cent stake in Ilmor engineering, which was formed by Mario Illien and Paul Morgan in 1983. Chevrolet paid for its nameplate to be included on the engine's cam covers, and reaped the benefits of being associated with six straight Indy 500 victories (1988–1993) and five

IndyCar championships (1988–1992).

Surprisingly, Chevrolet left IndyCar racing at the end of the 1993 season, just five days after Japanese car giant Honda announced its entry into the 1994 series.

The Chevrolet engine reverted to its original name, Ilmor, for the 1994 season, and another cam cover name seems likely to appear in time for the 1995

BELOW **Ilmor Indy V-8 engines power the Penske cars and a score of others. The engines had Chevrolet rocker covers until the car giant withdrew from IndyCar racing at the end of 1993.**

The newly developed Honda V-8 powers the Lolas of team-mates Bobby Rahal and Mike Groff. Although there have been no victories as at time of writing (mid-1994), no one doubts the Honda's winning potential.

season when Mercedes-Benz joins the fray. Mercedes-Benz has acquired a 20 per cent stake in Ilmor's North American affiliate, and a 25 per cent stake in Ilmor's British engineering firm. The company already has an established reputation at Indy races. In 1915 Ralph DePalma won the 500-mile classic, despite losing a connecting rod from the side of the crankcase with three laps to go, so strong was the engine.

Honda's entry into IndyCar racing is being run through Rahal-Hogan Team Miller. When Honda announced its intention

to enter the series many teams feared that its arrival in the sport would signal the end of fair competition, pointing out that Honda had dominated Formula 1 with the British McLaren team throughout the late 1980s and early 1990s. This fear led to some rather unsavoury tactics that appeared to restrict Honda's entry into the series – including the introduction of the minimum three cars, two teams rule – and at several stages Honda appeared on the verge of quitting.

In the first few races of 1994 Bobby Rahal and Mike Groff did not sweep the board. In fact,

Rahal's car failed to finish any of the races at the beginning of the season. However, no one doubts the might and resolve of Honda.

At the time of writing it would seem that two other Japanese car manufacturers, Toyota and Nissan, are preparing to compete in IndyCar racing before the end of the decade. The Toyota effort is being headed by Dan Gurney, whose teams swept IMSA sportscar racing for the Japanese manufacturer in the early 1990s, and it is aiming for a mid-1995 series debut.

Nigel Mansell, using Ford-Cosworth power, put an end to

RIGHT **Ford-Cosworth power put an end to Chevrolet's dominance of IndyCar racing in 1993, when Nigel Mansell used such a motor to take the PPG Cup.**

Chevrolet's recent dominance of IndyCar racing by winning the 1993 series championship. During the 1993 season Chevrolet speculated about the induction system used in the XB-designated engine. In the Ford-Cosworth, motor fuel is injected into the engine at two points: near each cylinder at the base of the turbocharger manifold and at the outer upstream face of the compressor. Chevrolet suggested that such a system was tantamount to intercooling,

which is banned in IndyCar racing.

Nevertheless, Mansell's five victories put the blue oval back in the winner's circle and on a series championship trophy.

RIGHT **This is a name to look out for. Dan Gurney will guide Toyota's entry into the sport with his American Eagle team, the same outfit that helped Toyota to two IMSA Championships.**

TYRES ARE TURNIN'

LEFT **Tyres are constantly checked and analysed. The temperature of this particular tyre is being checked with a pyrometer.**

❝IN 1922 GOODYEAR DROPPED OUT OF MOTOR RACING, STATING IT HAD **NOTHING LEFT TO PROVE**❞

Just as in virtually every other form of motor racing, Goodyear is the tyre of choice for most IndyCar teams.

Goodyear rubber has been around almost as long as people have been racing cars, with the company developing its first race tyre in 1902. An indication of just how good the first Goodyear race tyre actually was, may be gleaned from the fact that, using a straight-sided detachable tyre,

Barney Oldfield won 72 consecutive races in a 15-month period in 1905 and 1906. In 1919 Goodyear won every major motor racing event in North America, including the Indy 500, which was won by Howdy Wilcox and in which 27 of the 33 starters began the race on Goodyear rubber.

In 1922 Goodyear dropped out of motor racing, stating, with some justification, that it had

ABOVE **A crewman prises off loose rubber that has been picked up by the tyres during a practice session. Careful attention to tyre wear can mean the difference between winning and losing a race.**

"nothing left to prove". The company held true to its word for the next 32 years until, in 1954, it started a tyre-testing programme at Darlington Speedway for NASCAR's convertible sedan series. At the urging of A. J. Foyt, Goodyear commenced an Indy car tyre-development programme in 1963, and one year later Foyt drove to victory at the Phoenix 100, scoring Goodyear's first IndyCar win since 1919.

In 1984 Goodyear introduced its Eagle road course radial tyre at the Portland event and promptly won the race, with Al Unser Jr at the wheel. The short oval Eagle radial made its first appearance at the 1985 Milwaukee race, and this time Mario Andretti sped his way to victory. The radial line-up was completed in 1986 when the Superspeedway Eagle was used at the Pocono 500 race, and Mario Andretti again put the tyre in the winner's circle on its first competition run.

While Goodyear has dominated IndyCar racing since its return to the series in 1964, a potential challenger is on the horizon. Firestone, which last contested IndyCar races in 1975, will return to the sport in 1995, and during 1994 it conducted a test programme with drivers Al Unser Sr and Scott Pruett of Patrick Racing.

AERODYNAMICS

'THIS LOW-PRESSURE AREA EFFECTIVELY 'SUCKS' THE CAR DOWN ONTO THE TRACK'

ABOVE **Teams are always looking for ways to improve a car's aerodynamics, and this shark-fin design became an essential innovation in 1994 after it had first been seen on the Penske cars.**

While the engines produce the horsepower that propels the race cars around the track and, hopefully, into the winner's circle, it is the aerodynamics that help the car to achieve that win in the quickest time and in the most efficient way possible.

One of the most significant aerodynamic features on an Indy car is how best it uses ground effects. Ground effects are created by an air channel under the car, which forms a low-pressure area, or partial vacuum, between the car and the race track. This low-pressure area effectively "sucks" the car down onto the track. Of course, the ground effects tunnel is just one element of the entire aerodynamics package, the most visible parts of which are the front and rear wings, and these, when combined with the tunnel, create downforce.

Race teams spend a significant amount of their time at the track

RIGHT **For improved aerodynamics, Michael Andretti's Reynard features a dual-element front wing with an air-tunnel on each side of the nose, as does Mauricio Gugelmin's car below, but the wing on Claude Bourbonnais's Lola below right, looks less aerodynamic.**

trying to find the perfect "balance" for the car, which often means adjusting and changing the angle of the wings to best complement the ground effects tunnel and prevailing track conditions. On small oval tracks and road courses teams use large front wings to provide more downforce. The rear wings are a science in themselves, and

it is not uncommon for teams to try five or six elements within the section.

At Superspeedways downforce isn't so much a problem, simply because of the sheer speed the cars can achieve. The problem that has to be overcome at Super-speedways is drag, which must be reduced to achieve maximum speed, and as

a result the cars will run only one element on the rear wing.

Another important element to the overall aerodynamics package is the car's bodywork, which is made of carbonfibre. Included in a car's bodywork is the floor, nose piece, side pods, engine cover and monocoque. The bulky looking side pods, located either side of the driver,

RIGHT **Race teams make constant adjustments to their driver's car, including resetting the front wings to help improve handling.**

BELOW **The rear wings are also continually fine-tuned and adjusted. It is not uncommon for teams to try five or six elements within the cord section of a wing in the search for greater downforce.**

act as aerodynamic and protective covers for the car's radiators.

If the car's aerodynamic package isn't what it could be, it doesn't matter how much horsepower the engine may deliver, the odds are that the driver will not be sipping champagne at the end of the race.

TELEMETRY

Telemetry simply means the use of radio waves to transmit data. Each car is fitted with a black box that sends radio signals to an engineer in the pits. The information transmitted by the black box enables the engineer to determine how the car is performing around the track and to suggest possible changes to the chassis and engine that may improve performance.

Before the introduction of telemetry systems all communication between the driver and his crew had been by means of hand and pit boards.

ABOVE **Since the early 1980s IndyCar teams have relied on computers in the pits to analyse fuel consumption and car performance during races.**

The arrival of two-way radios improved matters by enabling drivers to communicate with their crew to discuss possible changes to the car during a race. Telemetry, however, has virtually eliminated the need for second-guessing the condition of chassis and engine set-ups – an instant computer analysis tells the crew what to change and when.

At the heart of a telemetry system is a Radio Telemetry Module (RTM) that houses a radio- and digital-card with a custom-built GM Motorsports Technology Group microprocessor. This package records two types of data: a lap summary, which includes peak temperatures, pressures and so forth, and statistical data, recorded during the course of one complete lap. The RTM is also capable of sending real-time information, which allows the engineer to read what is happening to the car as it actually happens.

IndyCar organizers were quick to recognize that, if it is possible to send information from the car to the pits, it is equally possible to send information the other way – from the pits to the car. Of course, such a facility would remove another human element from the sport, and the signals are therefore allowed to travel one way only: from the car to the pits.

HOW MUCH DID YOU SAY?

'RACING A MODERN-DAY INDYCAR IS NOT CHEAP. IN FACT IT IS DOWNRIGHT

Racing a modern-day Indy car is certainly not cheap. In fact, it's downright expensive.

Before a team can go racing it must purchase a chassis, of which there are currently three to choose from – Lola, Penske and Reynard – and although 15 of the season's 16 races are staged in North America (the race at Surfers Paradise in Australia is the odd one out), all of these chassis are built and manufactured in Britain. Of these three chassis, only two, Lola and Reynard, are available to customers. Penske chassis are available only to Roger Penske's team. A Lola and Reynard set back a team owner approximately $420,000

EXPENSIVE'

ABOVE **The transporters, cars, engines and ancillary equipment mean that it takes millions of dollars to maintain a competitive IndyCar team.**

LEFT **The typical IndyCar team trailer is a rolling workshop. This is Mike Groff's trailer, and behind the cabinet doors are enough parts to rebuild the complete racing car if necessary.**

(£280,000), for which he or she will receive what is commonly known as a rolling chassis. The rolling chassis consists of the monocoque tub, suspension and steering systems, wings and bodywork. That's it. No engine, dashboard, electronics, turbocharger, tyres or any other extras.

There are currently three engines to choose from: Ilmor, Ford-Cosworth and Honda. One of these will cost anywhere between $39,000 and $148,000 (£26,000–£100,000) and must be rebuilt every 400–500 miles (600–800 km) at an average cost of $28,000 (£18,000). The average IndyCar team will allocate between six and ten engines to each race car. Telemetry, electronics and so on will add another $750,000 (£500,000) to the cost of the car.

Not all IndyCar teams contest every race on the 16-event tour, but teams that plan to run at either Indianapolis Motor Speedway or Michigan International Speedway will have to purchase what is known as a speedway kit from the chassis manufacturer. This includes special wings and suspension components needed for travelling around the super-fast oval tracks, costs $60,000 (£40,000).

Remember, this is just for **one** race car. The team will need to purchase a second car in case the primary car is damaged, and possibly a third, which will be used for testing and development and a trailer for spare parts will add another $500,000 (£350,000).

Conservative estimates put the cost of joining the IndyCar ranks at $2.5 million (£1.6 million), while the high-profile teams will spend anything between $4 million (£2.6 million) and more than $15 million (£10 million) each year to race their cars.

CHAPTER THREE

TIMING AND PIT STOPS

ABOVE **Pit stops play a critical role in deciding the outcome of any IndyCar race. Crews will change all four wheels and add as much as 40 US gallons (151.4 litres) of fuel to their car in little more than 10 seconds.**

WHAT TIME IS IT?

One of the most critical elements of the Indy 500, and in particular in qualifying for the race itself, is accurately timing the race cars as they travel around the 2½-mile (4.1 km) track. Accurate timing not only allows the qualifying cars to be correctly placed, it also serves as an excellent source of information for the engineers who have to determine the cars' strengths and weaknesses on the course.

In 1927 T. J. Watson, founder of IBM, provided punch-card tabulating machines to Chester Rickers, the first director of Indianapolis Motor Speedway, to supplement the track's existing timing and scoring system. Although it was an improvement on the original timing and scoring system, this antiquated method remained in use until 1956, when C. E. "Eric" Ericksson introduced a pit-scoring system and conversion on which lap scorers could record times with a pencil. This apparently minor

'THE NEW SYSTEM ALLOWS STATISTICIANS TO MEASURE CORNERING SPEEDS AS WELL AS **TOP SPEEDS** ON THE STRAIGHTS'

improvement dramatically reduced the time taken to compile official results, which had previously taken hours or even days to prepare.

Ericksson was somewhat ahead of his time, because during the 1950s he also experimented with a prototype car-mounted radio transmitter to aid real-time timing data. He ultimately was thwarted because the radio technology of the time could not cope with his demands.

When computers began to make inroads into everyday life

in the 1960s, it was only a matter of time before the Speedway was using one, and in 1964 a mainframe computer was used for the first time and the punch-cards were scrapped.

The mainframe computer was the mainstay of the track's timing and scoring system until 1978, when Art Graham, a computer enthusiast, arrived on the scene. Graham had adapted his software to produce qualifying statistics at USAC races and introduced a similar package, known as ASCORE, into the Speedway operation. Graham continued to develop the program and in 1981 upgraded the system to include both qualifying and scoring functions. The system was enhanced in 1982, when Graham's brother, Andrew, adapted a personal computer to handle the multiple tasks within the USAC master scoring network.

The next significant improvement to the Speedway data gathering system came in

PIT STOP

RIGHT **During pit stops three nitrogen-powered, on-board, air-compressed jacks lift the car off the ground to assist in rapid tyre or wheel changes.**

1990, when the Dorian DATA-1 timing system was introduced. This system, designed by Australian Ian Chatwin, enables statisticians to plot car speed to 0.0001 seconds at any point on the track by using a combination of a car-borne radio transmitter, which sends timing information in real time, and the existing track-embedded receiving systems located around the track.

In the quest for even more information, the Integrated Race Information System, IRIS for short, was introduced in 1991 by the installation of seven additional track-embedded data gathering points. The new system allows statisticians to measure cornering speeds as well as top speeds on the straights.

Although it's the car that crosses the finish line first that decides who is the winner of a race, the most critical element of an IndyCar race is probably the pit stop. Because the cars are limited to 40 US gallons (151.4 litres) of methanol, pit stops are needed to refill the fuel cell, and while the car is in the pit stall the crew will also change all four tyres in an effort to give the driver improved traction. A quick, well-orchestrated pit stop can give a driver an edge over an opponent; a sloppy, disorganized pit stop can relegate a driver from first to last place in a matter of seconds.

When an Indy car enters pit lane for refuelling or other maintenance, a total of six crewmen are allowed over the pit wall to service the car. If the driver overshoots his designated pit area, the crewmen are allowed to pull the driver back to his stall provided they can safely do so and provided the driver hasn't overshot his pit area by more than one stall. If that happens, the driver has to make another lap of the race track and try again.

Once the car has stopped at its pit stall, a crewman will insert an air hose into the car which activates the car's on-board hydraulic jacks and lifts the chassis off the ground. Because time is of the essence, air wrenches are used to remove and refit the wheel nuts on wheel changes.

The largest consumer of time during most pit stops is refuelling, and it takes 10–15 seconds to get the methanol into the fuel cell. Two hoses are used for this process: one to pour the fuel into the car, the second to catch any spills and filter them back into the tank. Although methanol is less volatile than petrol, it can still catch fire, so all crewmen must wear fire-protective suits, while the two crewmen who help to refuel the car must also wear protective head wear.

Pit stops can take 15 or so seconds for a refuelling and tyre change, and they are performed with great precision. However, should a driver pull away from the pit area before the car is free of hoses and tools, or if he or she drives over any of the hoses , the driver will receive a stop-and-go penalty, meaning another visit to the pit lane.

DYNAMICS OF A PIT STOP

LEFT **Fuel is forced into the car through this opening. The small groove holds the nozzle to the car on the inward motion.**

In 10–15 seconds, most Indy car crews can add up to 40 gallons of fuel and change 4 tyres. The outside front tyre man posts himself so that the driver knows where to stop, then changes the right front tyre with a pneumatic air gun. When he has finished, he runs back to the pit wall so that the driver doesn't illegally run over his air hose. The right rear tyre man changes the tyre, then stands at the rear of the car and pushes off to help get the driver started. The left rear tyre changer simultaneously does the same. If the engine stalls, he grabs the starter and inserts it in the back of the car.

The jack man puts the air hose into the car jack port while also holding the fuel overflow hose which shows when the tank is filled. Then compressed nitrogen lifts the car off the pavement. The fueller positions the fuel hose and when the tank is full an automatic shut-off valve prevents the fuel from spilling when he pulls out the nozzle. Behind the wall, six other crewmen calculate fuel mileage, prepare tyres for changing and hold a valve open so that fuel can flow out of the storage tank. In the meantime, the team owner/manager talks to the driver by radio.

50

ABOVE **The crews of Al Unser Jr, near lane, and Mario Andretti compete at** Indianapolis Motor Speedway to see who can get their car out of the pits first.

INDY LIGHTS

ABOVE **All the teams competing in Indy Lights must use a Lola 93/20 chassis, a sealed Buick engine and Firestone tyres, which places the emphasis on driving ability rather than on the cars.**

ABOVE **Four-time FIM 500cc World Motorcycle Champion Eddie Lawson was a full-time competitor on the Indy Lights tour in 1994.**

ABOVE **Britain's Steve Robertson has been a formidable competitor on the Indy Lights tour and seems destined for future IndyCar fame.**

ABOVE **Young Greg Moore of Canada is another bright prospect currently in the Indy Lights ranks. In 1994, when he was just 18 years old, he won the Indy Lights race at Phoenix International Raceway.**

Jointly sponsored by PPG and Firestone, and known as the "Official Development Series", Indy Lights is where tomorrow's IndyCar stars are to be found.

Introduced in 1986 by U.E. "Pat" Patrick and Roger Bailey, the Indy Lights series places emphasis on driver ability rather than on whoever has the deepest pockets and the largest chequebook.

All the drivers compete in "spec", or identical cars. When the series was introduced the chassis used was a March 85B,

but in mid-1992, with interest in the series beginning to flag a little, it was argued, with some justification, that a March chassis no longer reflected the current trends in IndyCar racing. A new chassis was, therefore, commissioned for the beginning of the 1993 season – a Lola 93/20. Although many feared that introducing a new chassis would deter many potential participants, the opposite has been true, as the series is now better supported than ever.

It is not just the chassis for Indy Lights that are identical. All

> **'INDY LIGHTS IS WHERE TOMORROW'S INDYCAR STARS ARE TO BE FOUND'**

participating teams must use a sealed Buick V-6 engine, which delivers an estimated 425 horsepower and is provided to the series through a leasing

RIGHT **Steve Robertson (right) has already been a winner in Indy Lights racing. How long will it be before he is in the IndyCar winner's circle?**

FAR RIGHT **Tomorrow's IndyCar stars can be found today in the Indy Lights series, in which drivers compete against each other in identical cars.**

programme. Completing the package are four Firestone Firehawk tyres.

So does Indy Lights really deliver the IndyCar stars of tomorrow? The series' most notable graduate is Paul Tracy, who won the 1990 Indy Lights title and went on to join Roger Penske's team, with which he won five IndyCar races in 1993. Other rising stars include Mike Groff, the 1989 Indy Lights champion, who now drives for the Rahal/Hogan IndyCar team, and Adrian Fernandez, who is driving one of Rick Galles' entries in 1994.

The 1993 Indy Lights title was claimed by Bryan Herta, who drove one of Steve Horne's Tasman Motorsports Group entries to eight pole positions and seven event wins in the championship. Horne had also won two PPG IndyCar titles while with TrueSports in the 1980s.

PROFILES

INDYCAR CHAMPIONSHIP WINNERS

1909 George Robertson	1938 Floyd Roberts	1966 Mario Andretti
1910 Ray Harroun	1939 Wilbur Shaw	1967 A.J. Foyt
1911 Ralph Mulford	1940 Rex Mays	1968 Bobby Unser
1912 Ralph DePalma	1941 Rex Mays	1969 Mario Andretti
1913 Earl Cooper		1970 Al Unser Sr
1914 Ralph DePalma	1942 NO RACING	1971 Joe Leonard
1915 Earl Cooper	1943 NO RACING	1972 Joe Leonard
1916 Dario Resta	1944 NO RACING	1973 Roger McCluskey
1917 Earl Cooper	1945 NO RACING	1974 Bobby Unser
1918 Ralph Mulford	1946 Ted Horn	1975 A.J. Foyt
1919 Howard Wilcox	1947 Ted Horn	1976 Gordon Johncock
1920 Gaston Chevrolet	1948 Ted Horn	1977 Tom Senva
1921 Tommy Milton	1949 Johnnie Parsons	1978 Tom Senva
1922 Jimmy Murphy	1950 Henry Banks	1979 Rick Mears
1923 Eddie Hearne	1951 Tony Bettenhausen	1980 Johnny Rutherford
1924 Jimmy Murphy	1952 Chuck Stevenson	1981 Rick Mears
1925 Peter DePaolo	1953 Sam Hanks	1982 Rick Mears
1926 Harry Hartz	1954 Jimmy Bryan	1983 Al Unser Sr
1927 Peter DePaolo	1955 Bob Swelkert	1984 Mario Andretti
1928 Louis Meyer	1956 Jimmy Bryan	1985 Al Unser Sr
1929 Louis Meyer	1957 Jimmy Bryan	1986 Bobby Rahal
1930 Billy Arnold	1958 Tony Bettenhausen	1987 Bobby Rahal
1931 Louis Schneider	1959 Rodger Ward	1988 Danny Sullivan
1932 Bob Carey	1960 A.J. Foyt	1989 Emerson Fittipaldi
1933 Louis Meyer	1961 A.J. Foyt	1990 Al Unser Jr
1934 Bill Cummings	1962 Rodger Ward	1991 Michael Andretti
1935 Kelly Petillo	1963 A.J. Foyt	1992 Bobby Rahal
1936 Mauri Rose	1964 A.J. Foyt	1993 Nigel Mansell
1937 Wilbur Shaw	1965 Mario Andretti	1994 Al Unser Jr

DRIVER PROFILE

NIGEL MANSELL

LEFT **Nigel Mansell is a great attraction for other celebrities. Here, musician and film producer George Harrison (right), visits the pits at the Long Beach (California) Grand Prix.**

> 'WHEN MANSELL **WON ON HIS FIRST OUTING,** INTEREST IN THE SERIES WENT THROUGH THE ROOF '

Nigel Mansell's impact on the IndyCar series will never be accurately quantified. When the 1992 Formula 1 FIA World Champion announced that he was going IndyCar racing in 1993 interest in the series rose substantially, and when Mansell won on his first outing – at Surfers Paradise in Brisbane, Queensland, Australia – that interest went through the roof.

Winning the FIA Formula 1 world title in 1992 had capped a long struggle to the top of motor sport by Mansell, who came to prominence in 1979, when he won the International Trophy event at Silverstone as a member of the Unipart March Formula 3 team. The following year Mansell again drove for March in a Ralt-Honda Formula 2 before making his debut in Formula 1 at the Austrian Grand

Prix, as team-mate to Mario
Andretti in the Lotus team.
Mansell's first pole position was
at the North American (Dallas)
Grand Prix in 1984, and the
following year he won his first
event, driving his Williams team
entry to victory at the British
Grand Prix at Brands Hatch.

While he was driving for
Williams, Mansell established
himself as the most likely British
driver to win the FIA Formula 1
world title since James Hunt did
so in 1976. In 1986 Mansell was
involved in a titanic struggle for
the championship with Alain
Prost, ultimately losing to the
Frenchman by just two points.
The following year Mansell
hounded his Williams team-mate
Nelson Piquet of Brazil for the
title, until he suffered an
accident at the Japanese Grand
Prix and was forced to miss the
two final races of the season.

In 1989 Mansell left Williams
for Ferrari, and he won his first
race with Ferrari at the Brazilian
Grand Prix. After two years with
the famous Italian equipe, he
announced his retirement from
competitive motor racing. The

ABOVE **Since joining the
IndyCar tour in 1993,
Britain's Nigel Mansell
has been nothing short
of spectacular in the
North American series.**

retirement did not last long,
however, and the persuasive
Frank Williams talked Mansell
back into one of his cars.
Nevertheless, despite driving one
of the most competitive cars on
the tour, Mansell still could not
clinch the world championship
he desired. That honour went to
Ayrton Senna of Brazil.

Everything came together for
Mansell in 1992, and he

dominated the season to take the
FIA Formula 1 title in style,
winning nine events in all: South
Africa, Mexico, Brazil, Spain,
San Marino, France, Britain,
Germany and Portugal. He also
grabbed 14 number one
qualifying positions during the
racing season.

In a total of 181 Formula 1
career starts, Mansell had 30
victories but, on 18 September
1992 he announced his
retirement from the touring
circus again and headed for
North America and the Newman-
Haas team.

Mansell's defence of his
IndyCar crown in 1994 was
blighted by mechanical breakage
and sheer lack of pace when
compared to the lightening-quick
Penskes. Mansell did claim three
pole positions during the year, at
Surfers Paradise, Belle Isle, and
Michigan, but only finished in
the top five on four occasions.
Mansell's best finishes came at
Long Beach and Cleveland,
where he finished each race in
second place.

Midway through the season
speculation began to rise about

ABOVE **When Nigel Mansell joined the IndyCar series he was, as reigning Formula 1 World Champion expected to dominate on street courses. Somewhat surprisingly, however, most of his successes have come on oval tracks.**

Mansell's future with the Newman/Haas team, fuelled by a June appearance for the Williams Formula 1 team at the French Grand Prix. By season's end Mansell's future was confirmed: he wouldn't be back on the North American tour in 1995.

Although Mansell was only on the IndyCar tour for two seasons, his impact on the series will last for years to come.

FIA FORMULA ONE WORLD CHAMPIONS AT INDY

Mario Andretti	1965–78, 1980–94
Albert Ascari	1952
Jack Brabham	1961, 1964, 1970
Jim Clark	1963–67
Juan Manuel Fangio	1958
Nino Farina	1956–57
Emerson Fittipaldi	1984–94
Graham Hill	1966–68
Denis Hulme	1967–69, 1971
Nigel Mansell	1993–94
Nelson Piquet	1992–93
Jochen Rindt	1967–68
Jackie Stewart	1966–67

DRIVER PROFILE

A. J. FOYT

'NO ONE DRIVER IS MORE **SYNONYMOUS WITH THE OPEN-WHEEL** SERIES THAN FOYT'

ABOVE **The greatest IndyCar driver ever? That may be a subjective view, but no one will deny that A.J. Foyt's impact on the sport has been enormous.**

What Richard Petty is to NASCAR, what Don Garlits is to NHRA drag racing, A. J. Foyt is all and more to IndyCar racing. No one driver is more synonymous with the open-wheel series than Foyt.

Anthony Joseph Foyt's credentials are impressive. He has been IndyCar champion seven times (in 1960, 1961, 1963, 1964, 1967, 1975 and 1979) and he was the first driver to win the Indy 500 four times (in 1961, 1964, 1967 and 1977), but his motor sport triumphs don't begin and end with IndyCars. Foyt also won the NASCAR Daytona 500 in 1972 and, sharing driving duties with Dan Gurney, won the 1966 Le Mans 24-hour endurance race.

In fact, if it has got wheels and an engine, Foyt has probably driven it.

In a career that spanned five decades Foyt has raced with IndyCar, United States Auto Club (USAC), International Motor Sports Association (IMSA) and NASCAR and he has been a winner in virtually everything he has cared to try. Career victories include 41 USAC stock car wins, 29 sprint car wins, 20 midget (smaller versions of sprint cars) wins, seven NASCAR wins, seven sports car wins, and two USAC championship dirt car (larger versions of sprint cars) wins. Foyt also won the International Race of Champions (IROC) title in 1976 and 1977.

But it is in IndyCar that Foyt really shone, from his debut in 1957 to his retirement in 1993. Through the early 1960s Foyt was the man to beat, scoring his first IndyCar series event victory at DuQuoin in 1960 and his first Indy 500 title the following year, and in 1964 he won a staggering 10 events, including seven in a row.

Foyt remained one of the sport's leading drivers through

RIGHT **A.J. Foyt (right), one of IndyCar racing's all-time great drivers, offers advice to driver Davy Jones.**

the 1970s, but the opposition – and age – gradually began to creep up on him. After his last IndyCar victory at the Pocono 500 in 1981, Foyt did not visit the winner's circle again, although it should be pointed out that he ran a very limited schedule of events from 1980 through 1987.

In 1988 Foyt contested all but one of the season's events, and, although he was never a title contender, he appeared to be having tremendous fun. However, the smiles were replaced by

grimaces of pain in 1990 when his car went off the track at Road America and he suffered serious leg and foot injuries. At his first event after recovering from the effects of the accident, the 1991 Indy 500, Foyt stunned everyone by qualifying second.

Foyt announced a limited retirement, so that he could concentrate on oval events rather than on the road courses like Road America, which had so nearly ended his career.

In 1992, Foyt competed at the

Surfers Paradise Grand Prix in Australia, a temporary street course, but thereafter only raced at Indianapolis, before trying other drivers in his cars.

With rookie sensation Robby Gordon driving for his team in 1993, Foyt had planned to run as his team-mate at the Indy 500, but after making a lap of the Speedway on Pole Day (15 May), Foyt returned to the garage area and announced his retirement from competitive motor racing to the waiting media.

DRIVER PROFILE

PAUL TRACY

In many ways Paul Tracy's rise to stardom in IndyCar racing occurred in exactly the way the text books say it should. He began in local racing events when he was a youngster and worked his way through the ranks, before being recognized by one of the major racing teams as an undeniable talent.

Tracy came to prominence in 1985 when, at the age of 16, he won the Canadian Formula Ford championship. Two years later he broadened his experience by competing in a variety of series, including Sports Car Club of America (SCCA) Escort, Mosport 24-hour event and the BBC Grandstand for Formula Fords. His first step to the top came in 1988 when he won the American Racing Series (Indy Lights) event at Phoenix International Raceway, his debut in the series.

In 1990 Tracy was awarded the Bruce McLaren Trophy by the British Racing Drivers' Club, a

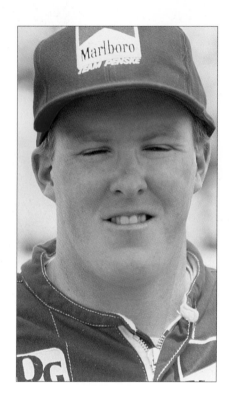

ABOVE **Canadian Paul Tracy is nothing if not spectacular at the wheel of one of Roger Penske's cars**

trophy that is presented annually to the Commonwealth's most promising racing drivers. Tracy was awarded the trophy on the strength of his Indy Lights championship title, when he won nine of the 14 events.

That same year Tracy got this first taste of true IndyCar racing when he tested one of the TrueSports entries. Team owner Dale Coyne was sufficiently impressed to put Tracy in one of his cars for the 1991 Long Beach Grand Prix, but by the middle of the year Tracy had joined Roger Penske's team as a test driver, and his status as one of the most prominent racing drivers in the world seemed assured.

Penske started Tracy in the Marlboro 500 at Michigan International Speedway, a race for which Tracy qualified an impressive eighth. However, the remainder of the event wasn't quite so memorable, and unfortunately on lap three Tracy crashed, breaking his left leg.

Tracy started 11 races in 1992, filling in for Rick Mears who crashed while qualifying for the Indy 500. When, at the end of the year, Mears surprisingly announced his retirement from

competitive motor racing, Tracy was his logical replacement

Throughout 1994 Tracy continued to build his reputation as one of IndyCar racing's fastest, if somewhat unpredictable, drivers. On his way to a third-place finish in the season standings, Tracy netted three No. 1 qualifying positions and nine top five finishes, including three firsts, at Belle Isle, Nazareth, and Laguna Seca.

Despite his impressive winning record, Tracy may not remain with the Penske team in 1995. Although team owner Roger Penske retains a one-year option on Tracy's services through 1995, the charismatic car owner/entrepreneur may revert back to a two-car team, leaving Tracy in the lurch.

However, before the last race of the 1994 season at Laguna Seca, Tracy already had impressed in an early-October test in one of the Bennetton Formula 1 cars, and reportedly has first refusal on the ride at Newman/Haas vacated by Nigel Mansell.

ABOVE **Paul Tracy made his debut for Roger Penske's high-powered team in 1991, qualifying eighth for the Marlboro 500 at Michigan International Speedway.**

❛AT THE **AGE OF 16,** HE WON THE CANADIAN FORMULA FORD CHAMPIONSHIP❜

DRIVER PROFILE

EDDIE CHEEVER

> 'IN 1990, CHEEVER WON THE ROOKIE OF THE YEAR TITLE ON THE STRENGTH OF **NINE TOP TEN FINISHES** '

Through the 1980s and 1990s only a few North American drivers have had the opportunity to try their luck in the heady world of Formula 1. Michael Andretti tried in 1993, and after proving so adept in the IndyCar series, he was expected to fly in Formula 1, but things didn't quite work out and Andretti quit just before the end of the season and returned to the North American IndyCar series.

One North American driver who proved he could run with the world's best – and probably would have been a consistent winner had he been given competitive machinery – is Eddie Cheever.

Cheever is a relatively new arrival to the IndyCar circuit, although he did appear in an open-wheel Indy car in 1986, driving for the Arciero team at the Miami Grand Prix. Cheever qualified 11th for the race but crashed on lap two – hardly an auspicious debut.

After making his Formula 1 debut for Tyrell in 1978 at the South African Grand Prix, Cheever went on to record a further 131 career starts in the FIA touring series. After Tyrell came sessions with Ligier, Renault, Alfa Romeo and then, finally, Arrows.

Following his IndyCar debut in Miami in 1986, Cheever briefly returned to Formula 1,

ABOVE **Eddie Cheever is one of only a handful of North American drivers to have competed in both IndyCar and Formula One in recent years.**

standing in for Patrick Tambay at the Detroit Grand Prix in a car owned by Carl Haas.

His open-wheel career apparently on hold, Cheever turned his attentions to

endurance racing, and in 1987 and 1988 he drove a variety of the full-bodied creations, most notably for Jaguar, for which he won an impressive seven FIA World Sports Car events.

In 1990 Cheever returned to IndyCars and won the Rookie of the Year title on the strength of nine Top Ten finishes. Cheever's best finish in an Indy car came in 1992, when he drove one of Chip Ganassi's entries to second place at Phoenix, Arizona.

Throughout 1993 Cheever hopped from team to team, driving for four different car owners, ending with Kenny Bernstein.

After beginning the 1994 season without a car to drive, Cheever ended the year at the wheel of A. J. Foyt's Lola after replacing injured Bryan Herta in Michigan. Cheever's best finish in his short season came at Vancouver, where he finished 17th.

ABOVE **At the 1994 Indianapolis 500 Eddie Cheever drove for the Menard team. Cheever made his IndyCar debut in 1986 at the wheel of one of Frank Arciero's cars.**

DRIVER PROFILE

MARIO ANDRETTI

One of motor racing's all-time great careers came to an end in 1994 when Mario Andretti hung up his firesuit and crash helmet after a lifetime in the fast lane.

Born in Montona, Italy, Andretti began driving racing cars when he was just 13 years old, competing in the Formula Junior ranks. When his family moved to the United States a couple of years later, Andretti found that his racing career would flourish in the new country, his first race being in 1958 at the wheel of a dirt-modified entry.

Andretti's IndyCar debut was in 1964 at Trenton, New Jersey, and in the following year he made his debut at Indianapolis Motor Speedway, qualifying fourth and

ABOVE **Mario Andretti drove a wide variety of racing cars – including sprint and NASCARs and Formula 1 – before becoming a mainstay of the IndyCar circuit.**

finishing an impressive third on his way to claiming the race's Rookie of the Year title. The successes didn't end there, however, for Andretti went on to claim the 1965 IndyCar championship title.

The ever-versatile Andretti was IndyCar champion again in 1966, and he went on to driving successes in other areas of the sport. In 1967 he won the NASCAR Daytona 500 race and the 12-hour Sebring endurance race. The following year Andretti made his Formula 1 debut at Watkins Glen. In 1969 he won the Indy 500, his only victory at IndyCar's premier event.

Despite numerous successes in his adopted country, Formula 1 still beckoned, and in 1971 Andretti won his first Formula 1 event, in South Africa at the wheel of a Ferrari.

Throughout the 1970s Andretti proved himself to be one of the most versatile drivers ever seen, winning four endurance events in 1972: the 6-hour Daytona Continental; a 1,000 km. (620 mile) competition at Brands Hatch; a 6-hour race at Watkins

'ANDRETTI BEGAN DRIVING RACING CARS WHEN HE WAS JUST 13 YEARS OLD'

Glen, and the 12-hour Sebring race for a second time.

Despite these successes, Andretti continued to compete in the often brutal world of dirt-track sprint car racing, and in 1974 he won the USAC title.

In 1978 Andretti achieved what

LEFT **The year 1994 was known as "Arrivederci, Mario", for Mario Andretti retired from competitive IndyCar racing at the end of the season.**

every racing driver yearns for: the FIA Formula 1 world title. Driving for Colin Chapman's Lotus team, Andretti became only the second North American driver to win the prestigious championship (Phil Hill was the first).

Although he was unsuccessful in defending his FIA world championship in 1979, Andretti proved himself one of the more adept drivers in the world when he won the International Race of Champions (IROC) title. The IROC series places racing drivers from a variety of disciplines (IndyCar, NASCAR, Formula 1 and so on) in identically prepared, full-bodied cars at race tracks across North America.

Andretti joined the Newman-Haas team in 1983, and the following year he won the IndyCar championship. In 1989 he was joined on the team by his son, Michael, with whom he had driven only once before as a team-mate: at the Le Mans 24-hour endurance race in 1983.

Although somewhat overshadowed by the presence of Nigel Mansell in the Newman-Haas team in 1993, Andretti left no doubt about which of them was the faster – during qualifying for the Marlborough 500 at Michigan International Speedway Andretti recorded the fastest lap ever by an Indy car: 234.275 mph (376.948 kph).

Andretti's final year at the wheel of an Indy car didn't go as the veteran driver had hoped. Andretti scored only three top five finishes during the year, the best of which was third-place at the opening race of the season at Surfers Paradise. His last race, at Laguna Seca, ended prematurely when the transmissions on his Lola broke several laps short of the checkered flag.

RIGHT **Mario Andretti behind the wheel of his Newman-Haas Lola.**

DRIVER PROFILE

ROBBY GORDON

If it's versatility you're looking for in a race driver, you'd be hard-pressed to find anyone who has driven a wider variety of vehicles than Robby Gordon.

Gordon began driving Indy cars in 1992 for Chip Ganassi's team at the urging of Ford's Special Vehicle Operations boss Michael Kranefaus. In 1993 he drove for the legendary A.J. Foyt and, in 1994, was at the wheel of one of Derrick Walker's entries. However, before embarking on a career in IndyCars, Gordon seemed destined to become one of the racing world's better "off-road" drivers.

His first taste of racing came when he was seven years old when he was riding a motocross motorcycle. He soon became an expert desert racer, and in 1985, aged 16, won the first off-road race he entered, the Nevada 500. Two weeks later Gordon was back in the winner's circle, this

ABOVE **One of several new young drivers to become involved in IndyCar racing in the 1990s is Robby Gordon, who, after a season with A. J. Foyt in 1993, joined Derrick Walker's outfit for 1994.**

time having won his first Mickey Thompson Entertainment Group (MTEG) stadium race.

In the latter half of the 1980s Gordon established himself as one of the hottest properties in off-road racing, claiming back-to-back SCORE and High Desert Racing Association titles in 1986 and 1987; in 1988 he won the MTEG 1600 Super Sport championship; and in 1989 he won what is probably the highest profile title in off-road racing, the MTEG Grand National stadium title for sport trucks, driving a factory-supported Toyota. Proving he was as good in the deserts as he was in packed football stadiums, Gordon also won the prestigious Baja 1000 off-road endurance race.

At the turn of the decade Gordon began trying his hand at other motor sports disciplines, driving one of Jack Roush's IMSA GTO Mercury Cougars to the class win in the Daytona 24-hour endurance race. Gordon proved fast when he was going in circles, too. On his first career start in an ARCA stock car (similar to NASCAR), Gordon qualified on the pole position.

ABOVE **Not only can Robby Gordon drive a 200 mph (322 kph) IndyCar, he is an accomplished off-road racer, having once driven for Toyota's factory team.**

Suitably encouraged, in the following year he qualified for the NASCAR Daytona 500, and, on his first start in the race, finished a respectable 18th before joining the ranks of IndyCar racing in 1992.

In 1994 Gordon made sterling efforts at the wheel of his Valvoline Lola. The Californian driver achieved two pole positions, both in Canada, at Toronto and Vancouver, and finished in the top five six times, with his best result also coming in Vancouver, where he finished second.

'GORDON SEEMED **DESTINED** TO BECOME ONE OF THE RACING WORLD'S BETTER 'OFF-ROAD' DRIVERS'

RIGHT **Robby Gordon is fast in any kind of vehicle. Here he puts Derrick Walker's Lola through its paces at Phoenix International Raceway.**

DRIVER PROFILE

RAUL BOESEL

> 'BOESEL WAS A **CONSTANT THORN IN THE SIDE** OF THE MORE ESTABLISHED INDYCAR STARS'

Brazilian Raul Boesel had aspirations of joining fellow-countrymen Ayrton Senna and Emerson Fittipaldi as one of the all-time great Formula 1 drivers before he actually found his home in IndyCar racing.

Boesel began driving Formula 1 cars for March Engineering in 1982, before moving to the French Ligier team the following year. Before joining motor sport's ultimate travelling circus Boesel had hoped to follow his brothers into show-jumping, but he found that driving go-karts provided more thrills than thoroughbred horses could provide.

After winning the Brazilian go-kart title when he was 17 years old, Boesel moved to Britain in 1980 and practised his craft at the wheel of Formula Fords, eventually winning the Royal Automobile Club Motor Sport Association's national championship.

Unable to find a competitive and regular ride in any particular motor sport discipline, Boesel skipped from Indy cars to endurance cars and back again through the latter half of the 1980s. After making his IndyCar debut for Dick Simon Racing in 1985, Boesel drove one of Tom Walkinshaw's Jaguars at the FIA world endurance championship in 1987.

Despite proving himself a more than capable driver of virtually any racing car he chose

ABOVE **Raul Boesel made his IndyCar debut at Long Beach in 1985, and he was the fastest rookie qualifier at Indianapolis later the same year.**

to sit in, Boesel still could not find the permanent ride he was looking for. In 1989 he drove for Doug Shierson's team, and in 1990 he piloted one of Norm Turley's TrueSports entries.

Boesel's next championship came at the wheel of a Jaguar, in which he drove his way to the

ABOVE **After replacing the injured Hiro Matsushita in the 1992 Indy 500, Raul Boesel became a permanent member of the Dick Simon Racing team.**

1991 IMSA GTP title. However, when Simon asked Boesel to replace the injured Hiro Matsushita for the 1992 Indy 500, his IndyCar aspirations took a turn for the better. Boesel was able to secure funding for the remainder of the season and, in 1993, with sponsorship from Duracell Batteries, he was a constant thorn in the side of the more established IndyCar stars.

After doing so well in 1993, Boesel had hoped for bigger and better things in 1994 but ultimately had to settle for just three top five finishes, at Long Beach, New Hampshire, and Nazareth, ending fourth at all three. Before the end of the season there were rumblings that Boesel would leave Simons' team and, for 1995, he will indeed have a new team-mate and a new team: Bobby Rahal and the Rahal/Hogan equipe.

DRIVER PROFILE

DANNY SULLIVAN

OK, so beginning your motor racing career as a janitor, cab driver, waiter, lumberjack, sod carrier and chicken ranch hand may not be everybody's idea of perfect schooling, but for Danny Sullivan it worked out just fine.

Sullivan began racing in Britain in 1972, at the wheel of Formula 3 cars, and he stayed on the European circuit for the next five years, competing with a variety of cars, including in Formula 3 and Formula 2 events and with the seemingly obligatory endurance machines.

In 1978 Sullivan ran some Formula Atlantic events in New Zealand and his native United States, contested the Can-Am series in 1981 and made his IndyCar debut at Atlanta Motor Speedway in 1982, when he finished third.

Driving for Tyrell in 1983 made Sullivan one of only a handful of North American drivers to have competed in Formula 1 in the 1980s, but after just one year on the globe-trotting FIA circuit, he returned to IndyCars.

Sullivan's return to the domestic series came with Doug Shierson's outfit, and he had his first IndyCar victory at Cleveland later that same year. After a year with Shierson, Sullivan joined Roger Penkse's team and went on to win the Indy 500 race, despite spinning out in front of Mario Andretti on lap 120. In 1988 he won the IndyCar series championship on the strength of four wins and nine pole positions.

However, all good things must come to an end, and in 1990 Sullivan left the Penske team, but not before posting a victory at the final race of the season at Laguna Seca (California).

In 1991 Sullivan teamed up

'**NOT EVERYBODY'S IDEA OF PERFECT SCHOOLING,** BUT FOR DANNY SULLIVAN IT WORKED OUT JUST FINE'

with Pat Patrick Racing, and in 1992 he joined the Galles-Kraco entourage, with help from sponsor Molson Breweries of Canada, as team-mate to Al Unser Jr.

For 1994 Sullivan's career appears to have taken yet another dramatic change: after a decade of driving open-wheel Indy cars, Sullivan ran a limited NASCAR schedule at the wheel of one of Felix Sabate's cars.

ABOVE **Danny Sullivan
(far right) is another of
that rare breed of
North American drivers
who have competed in
both Formula 1 and
IndyCar.**

DRIVER PROFILE

EMERSON FITTIPALDI

Emerson Fittipaldi is one of just three drivers to have won both the FIA Formula 1 world championship and IndyCar series titles. (Mario Andretti and Nigel Mansell are the other two.)

Like many world-class racing drivers, Fittipaldi got serious about his racing in Britain after originally cutting his teeth in his native country. After winning the Brazilian Vee title in 1967, Fittipaldi moved to Britain in 1969 to participate in a Formula Ford series. His driving talents were quickly recognized, and in 1970 he drove in the first of five Grand Prix events, driving for the Lotus team.

It was the beginning of a short period in which Fittipaldi established himself as one of motor racing's all-time great drivers, winning the FIA Formula 1 world title in 1972, being runner-up to the title in 1973 and winning the title again

ABOVE **At the start of the 1994 season Brazil's Emerson Fittipaldi had won 20 IndyCar events and captured 15 pole positions.**

in 1974, at the wheel of a McLaren.

Fittipaldi retired from active motor racing in 1982, but he was lured out of retirement in 1984 to take a stab at IndyCar racing. Liking the experience, he

remained with the sport, winning his first event at Michigan International Speedway in 1985. In 1988 he came second in the Indy 500, but won motor racing's biggest single event in the following year before going on to take the 1989 IndyCar series title.

Fittipaldi's title was significant not only because he was, at the time, only the second person to be both Formula 1 and IndyCar champion, but also because it was the first time that a non-North American driver had won a major North American domestic racing series title.

Like many high-profile racing drivers, Fittipaldi has many interests outside the sport, and he is widely regarded as an accomplished businessman. Through one of his many companies, Fittipaldi exports orange concentrate from his native Brazil to North America, Europe and Asia, and his love of

ABOVE **The crew warm up the engine of Emerson Fittipaldi's car**

orange juice brought down on him the wrath of middle American race fans after his dramatic victory at the 1993 Indy 500. In the winner's circle, Fittipaldi shunned the traditional drink of milk for a glass of orange juice.

Never at a loss for words, Fittipaldi speaks five languages fluently: English, Spanish, Italian, French, and his native Portuguese.

Through 1994 Fittipaldi continued to show his command of the Indy cars, piloting one of Penskes all-conquering entries to 11 top-five placings, including a victory at Phoenix, and four runner-up finishes.

'**NEVER AT A LOSS FOR WORDS,** FITTIPALDI SPEAKS FIVE LANGUAGES FLUENTLY'

OVERLEAF **Emerson Fittipaldi in his Penske Ilmor.**

DRIVER PROFILE

ARIE LUYENDYK

While Britain's Nigel Mansell may hog all the limelight as the best that European motor racing has to offer – and he was the defending FIA Formula 1 world champion when he joined the IndyCar ranks in 1993 – arguably the best European driver on the domestic series trail prior to Mansell's arrival was Dutchman Arie Luyendyk.

You have to look hard to find much mention of the popular Dutch driver in the annals of European motor racing, but Luyendyk is there. In 1975 he took the European Formula Ford title, and in 1977 he won the European Super Vee championship.

> '**ARGUABLY THE BEST EUROPEAN** DRIVER ON THE DOMESTIC SERIES' TRAIL PRIOR TO MANSELL**'**

LEFT Arie Luyendyk has found motor racing fame easier to come by in the United States than he did at home in the Netherlands.

ABOVE Before Nigel Mansell arrived on the IndyCar scene, Dutchman Arie Luyendyk was the leading European driver in the series.

But it was not until Luyendyk began racing cars in North America that he really began to attract attention. In 1984 he won the United States Super Vee title and in the same year made his IndyCar debut at Elkhart Lake. The following year Luyendyk completed a full season on the hectic IndyCar tour and was rewarded with the series Rookie of the Year title, ending the season with five Top Ten finishes. To complete his success, Luyendyk also received Rookie of the Year for his seventh-place finish at the Indy 500.

Through the latter half of the decade Luyendyk went on to achieve a succession of Top Five finishes that established him as one of the most consistent drivers in the sport, but it was not until 1990, when he joined Doug Shierson's team, that success finally arrived. In what is still a best-ever year for the European, Luyendyk posted 10 Top Ten finishes and at last won his first IndyCar event – the big one, at Indianapolis. Luyendyk's Indy 500 victory remains the fastest Indianapolis Motor Speedway victory on record; he averaged 185.981 mph (299.243 kph) for the 500-mile race.

In 1991 Luyendyk changed teams, joining Vince Granatelli's outfit, and again found his way to the winner's circle, at Phoenix, Arizona, and at Nazareth, Pennsylvania. After a year on the sidelines in 1992 Luyendyk teamed up with Chip Ganassi for the 1993 campaign, the highlight of the year coming when he won pole position for the Indy 500 and finished a strong second in the race.

Driving for the Eurosport-Boost Monaco team in 1994, Luyendyk's best finish of the year came in Michigan, where he piloted the car to a runner-up placing.

RIGHT **The Indianapolis Motor Speedway is one of Arie Luyendyk's favourite tracks. He won the 500-mile race in 1990, driving for Doug Shierson, and was second in 1993 in one of Chip Ganassi's cars.**

DRIVER PROFILE

AL UNSER JR

When Al Unser Jr entered the motor racing scene no one doubted his pedigree. The son of four-time Indy 500 champion Al Unser and nephew of three-time Indy 500 champion Bobby Unser, Little Al, as he became known, has been successful at virtually all forms of motor racing he has cared to try his hand at.

Beginning, as many youngsters do, with go-karts, Little Al's first experience of truly competitive racing came with the World of Outlaws, a group of sprint car drivers who travel around North America looking and racing for the largest purses they can find.

After two years' driving the unpredictable sprint cars, Unser joined Rick Galles' Super Vee team in 1981 and won the national championship, earning the Sports Car Club of America (SCCA) Rookie of the Year award for his efforts.

The following year, at the age

ABOVE **From go-karts and World of Outlaws sprinters to IndyCar champion, Al Unser Jr is one of North America's best open-wheel drivers.**

of 20, Unser got his first shot at IndyCar competition, taking part in the Riverside (California) 500 and scoring an impressive fifth-place finish. His first IndyCar victory came in 1984 at Portland, Oregon, and one year later he was denied the series title when he finished second to his father by just one point.

Also in 1985 Unser began to

expand his horizons, winning an IMSA-sanctioned three-hour endurance race at Daytona. In 1986 he won the International Race of Champions (IROC) title and a year later won the Le Mans 24-hour endurance race in which he shared driving duties with Al Hobert, Derek Bell and Chip Robinson.

Unser's success in the IROC series has helped him earn the respect of many of the NASCAR drivers – including perennial champion Dale Earnhardt – at whose race tracks (Super-speedways) most of the IROC events are contested.

After scoring his second IROC championship in 1988, Unser returned to IndyCars, securing a career-first pole position during qualifying for the Long Beach (California) Grand Prix. Later that year he seemed destined to win his first Indy 500 race, but, in lap 199 of 200, he touched wheels with rival Emerson

RIGHT **Al Unser Jr comes from a famous racing family. Both his father, Al Sr, who is seen here at the wheel of one of the Porsche Indy cars in 1987, and his uncle, Bobby, have raced in North America's premier open-wheel series.**

INDY 500 TRIVIA

Youngest winner:	Troy Ruttman in 1952
	22 years, 2 months
Oldest winner:	Al Unser Sr in 1987
	47 years, 11 months
Largest winning margin:	Jule Goux over Spencer Wishart in 1913
	13 minutes, 8 seconds
Closest winning margin:	Al Unser Jr over Scott Goodyear in 1992
	0.043 seconds
Fastest winning speed:	185.981 mph (299.243 kph)
	Arie Luyendyk in 1990
Slowest winning speed:	74.602 mph (120.034 kph)
	Ray Harroun in 1911

❛HE WAS **DENIED THE SERIES TITLE** WHEN HE FINISHED SECOND TO HIS FATHER BY JUST ONE POINT❜

Fittipaldi and spun out. Fittipaldi went on to win the race and in a sportsman-like gesture, Unser applauded his opponent's victory.

In 1990 Unser drove his way to the IndyCar series title, winning six of 16 races on the tour. One of those victories came at the super-fast Michigan International Speedway, where Unser won the fastest 500-mile race on record, averaging a stunning 189.727 mph (305.27 kph).

After the disappointment of losing the 1989 Indy 500 on the penultimate lap, Unser was one half of one of the greatest Indy events of record. In 1992 he barely held off Canadian Scott Goodyear to win the 500-mile classic by a mere .043 seconds.

In 1994 Unser joined Roger Penske's team in the Marlboro-backed entries, the same team with which his father and uncle had enjoyed so much success and repeated his Indianapolis victory with another win in May.

Throughout 1994 Unser dominated IndyCar racing. On the strength of his Indy 500 victory Unser assumed the lead

of the season's points and was never overtaken. In a career season, his first for Roger Penske, Unser scored 11 top-five finishes, including eight race victories at: Long Beach, Indianapolis, Milwaukee, Portland, Cleveland, Mid-Ohio, New Hampshire, and Vancouver.

'UNSER WAS ONE HALF OF **ONE OF THE GREATEST INDY EVENTS ON RECORD**'

ABOVE **Al Unser Jr's racing experience covers IROC, NASCAR and endurance sports cars and even Formula 1 with some success.**

DRIVER PROFILE

BOBBY RAHAL

Six months after winning the 1992 IndyCar series title, Bobby Rahal was forced to sit through one of the most humbling moments of his long and illustrious career: with time running out for qualifying for the Indy 500, Rahal could only watch as his Miller Genuine Draft-sponsored entry was systematically knocked down the qualifying ladder and, ultimately, off it.

Rather than making a scene, as many other drivers would have done in similar circumstances, Rahal shrugged at the television camera inches from his face and dismissed the situation as "simply racing".

This quiet demeanour has enabled Rahal to earn the respect of his peers while establishing himself as one of the sport's more analytical and competent drivers.

After winning the Formula Atlantic title in 1975, Rahal tasted the glamour of Formula 1 with the not-so-glamourous Wolf team, driving at Watkins Glen and in Montreal. In 1982 he made his IndyCar series debut in Phoenix, Arizona, won his first career race at Cleveland and finished a creditable second in the series-long chase. As if there was any doubt, Rahal was named Rookie of the Year.

Like many other IndyCar regulars, Rahal also tried the 24-hour Le Mans endurance race in 1983, but unfortunately he didn't

RAHAL SHRUGGED HIS SHOULDERS AT THE TELEVISION CAMERA INCHES FROM HIS FACE AND DISMISSED THE SITUATION AS

'SIMPLY

RIGHT **Bobby Rahal became a team owner in 1992 when he joined forces with Carl Hogan, winning the PPG Cup in his first season as an owner-driver.**

RACING'

finish the race. The following
year, to broaden his experience,
Rahal drove one of the Wood
Brothers' NASCAR entries at
Riverside, California.

Through the latter half of the
decade Rahal became one of the
drivers to beat in North
America's premier domestic
open-wheel series, and in 1986
he won the IndyCar series crown.
To prove that was no fluke, he
repeated the feat for spectators
the following year.

Believing that the only way to
compete with the likes of Carl

Haas and Roger Penske, Rahal,
along with business partner Carl
Hogan, purchased the Patrick
team in 1991. After winning the
IndyCar series title for a third
time in 1992, Rahal struggled
through much of 1993 and,
towards the end of the season,
formally announced that his
team would head Honda's entry
into the series in 1994.

Two-thirds of the way through
a forgettable 1994 season, Rahal
announced that in 1995 the
Rahal Hogan team would no
longer use the Honda engines,

ABOVE **Bobby Rahal and
the crew discuss the
handling of the unique
Honda-powered Lola
after a practice session
at Phoenix
International Raceway.**

switching, instead, to the tried-
and-tested Ilmore-built Mercedes.

The season was not without its
occasional high point: Rahal
finished third at the Indy 500,
albeit with an Ilmor-engined car,
and drove the Honda to its best
finish, a second place, at Toronto.

RIGHT **Bobby Rahal and the crew discuss the handling of the unique Honda-powered Lola after a practice session at Phoenix International Raceway.**

6ONE OF THE SPORT'S MORE ANALYTICAL AND COMPETENT DRIVERS9

LEFT **Before becoming a Championship-winning owner-driver in 1992, Bobby Rahal won PPG Cup titles in both 1986 and 1987. Rahal is pictured at Laguna Seca on his way to his second series title.**

DRIVER PROFILE

SCOTT GOODYEAR

No one disputes Canadian Scott Goodyear's talents as a racing driver. In his native country, he has won the prestigious Canadian Racing Drivers Association Driver of the Year title no fewer than three times (in 1980, 1986 and 1992). However, it is only since the early 1990s that Goodyear has established himself as one of IndyCar's better drivers. Although Goodyear made sporadic appearances in the open-wheel racing series in 1987 (seven times) and 1989 (twice), it was not until 1990, when he was driving for the Mackenzie Financial team, that he became a household name.

Before turning to IndyCars, Goodyear established himself as a very versatile driver, winning Canadian and North American go-kart titles between 1969 and 1976 and becoming the Formula Ford driver to beat in Canadian racing. Between 1980 and 1982

ABOVE **While he was driving for Derrick Walker, Canadian Scott Goodyear (left) lost the 1992 Indy 500 race to Al Unser Jr by a margin of less than half a second. In 1994 Goodyear drove for drag racer Kenny Bernstein.**

Goodyear won three consecutive Formula Ford championships. Broadening his horizons Goodyear took part in some Formula 2000 and saloon-car Trans Am races in 1983 before joining the Tom Mitchell Racing Formula Atlantic team in 1986.

In what proved to be a pivotal career move, Goodyear scored five pole positions and five event wins in nine starts while on his way to taking the series title.

Without a regular IndyCar ride, Goodyear continued to impress in a variety of other disciplines, driving one of Jack Roush's GTO Mustangs to third place at the Daytona 24-hour endurance race in 1987, and winning the Rothmans Porsche Turbo Cup series championship in 1988.

After driving for the factory-backed Audi Sport team in IMSA GTO races in 1989, Goodyear arrived on the IndyCar scene and scored nine Top Ten finishes in his first full season on the senior tour.

Goodyear consolidated his reputation as a consistent driver in 1991 before having his best season yet in 1992. On his way to finishing fifth in the end-of-

RIGHT **The Budweiser King team was expected to be a force to be reckoned with in 1994 with Scott Goodyear at the wheel, but early season expectations were not realized.**

season points table, he almost won the Indy 500 race, failing to catch winner Al Unser Jr by just 0.043 seconds after starting the race last. Obviously disappointed at losing the Indy race by such a small margin, Goodyear bounced back a few weeks later to score a deserved victory at the Marlboro 500 at Michigan International Speedway.

After such promise in 1992 the following season was not particularly spectacular, although Goodyear still finished an impressive eighth in the

series' points chase, and for 1994 joined drag racer Kenny Bernstein's Budweiser King outfit.

It was expected that Goodyear and the Budweiser car should have been one of the combinations to beat in 1994, but the promised threat never materialized. Ironically, Goodyear won the Michigan 500 just days after team owner Bernstein announced that he would withdraw from IndyCar racing which left Goodyear without a car at the end of the 1994 season.

'HE **ALMOST WON** THE INDY 500, FAILING TO CATCH WINNER AL UNSER BY JUST 0.043 SECONDS **AFTER STARTING THE RACE LAST**'

DRIVER PROFILE

TEO FABI

What do former downhill skiers do when they're looking for a new challenge? Well, if they are like Italy's Teo Fabi, they go motor racing.

Trained as an aeronautical engineer with a degree from the Institute of Technology in Milan, Italy, Fabi has driven everything from Formula 1 to Group C endurance and IndyCars. It would be difficult to find anyone as versatile in a variety of high-performance machines.

After winning the 1976 European go-kart title, Fabi won the Italian Formula Ford championship the following year, finishing fourth in the European title chase. Beginning first as a test, and later as a race driver for March, Fabi tested the waters of Formulas Two and Three before joining Paul Newman's SCCA Can-Am team in 1981. The following season Formula 1 beckoned, and Fabi

'IT WOULD BE DIFFICULT TO FIND ANYONE AS **VERSATILE** IN A VARIETY OF HIGH-PERFORMANCE MACHINES'

LEFT **Teo Fabi took pole position for the Indy 500 in 1988, his rookie year and only his second start in such a car.**

joined the Toleman team before joining the IndyCar ranks in 1983.

Fabi made his IndyCar debut at Atlanta Motor Speedway and carved a place for himself in the trivia books when, in qualifying for the Indy 500, he qualified on the pole position, the first time a rookie had achieved such a feat. Fabi even led the 500-mile race until a fuelling malfunction put paid to his chances, but he had already done enough to earn the race's Rookie of the Year award.

Proving that his Indy success was no fluke, Fabi continued to challenge for the series title, eventually finishing second to Al Unser but still amassing enough points to win the series' Rookie of the Year award.

Despite his undoubted ability in the IndyCars, Fabi returned to Formula 1 in 1984, driving for Brabham, then for Toleman in 1985 and, finally, for Benneton in 1986. In 1988 Fabi was appointed lead driver in Porsche's IndyCar effort, finishing 10th in the points listings at the end of the season. In the following year he helped Porsche to score its only IndyCar series event victory, at Mid-Ohio, a race which Fabi won from the pole position.

When Porsche dropped its

IndyCar programme, Fabi returned to the Group C entries, helping Jaguar to its FIA World Sportscar Championship title in 1991. In 1992 Fabi made a rare, one-race appearance in a Newman-Haas entry, standing in for an injured Michael Andretti at the Detroit Grand Prix.

For 1993 Fabi replaced John Andretti in the Jim Hall entry, and although success has been hard to come by, many pundits pick them as the team most likely to succeed.

At the end of 1994 Fabi

ABOVE **Not all of Teo Fabi's memories of Indianapolis are happy ones. In 1988 he spun and crashed while entering his pit area.**

announced he would be leaving the Hall team after putting in another workman-like season. Fabi drove the Pennzoil-backed Reynard to three fourth-place finishes, at Belle Isle, Michigan, and Elkhart Lake, and a fifth place at Laguna Seca, his last drive in the car.

DRIVER PROFILE

MICHAEL ANDRETTI

It is probable that Michael Andretti would just as soon forget his brief flirtation with Formula 1 when, during a nightmare 1993 season, he was dogged by bad luck at the McLaren team. Most observers agreed that Andretti had been given a raw deal, and the media made sure Andretti relived every moment of it.

When Andretti quit the McLaren team in September, announcing that he would be joining Chip Ganassi's outfit which, for 1994, would be using the all-new but as yet untested Reynard chassis, the same media hounds predicted it would be another miserable year for the 1991 IndyCar series champion.

How wrong they were. Defying his critics, Andretti led from start to finish in the 1994 IndyCar season opener at Surfers Paradise in Brisbane, Queensland, Australia, and Nigel Mansell's worst nightmare had come true.

ABOVE **Michael Andretti didn't have much to smile about during his few months in Formula 1 in 1993, but he returned to IndyCar with a great win in Australia in the first race of the 1994 season.**

Andretti began driving go-karts in the early 1970s before entering his first official competition, a Formula Ford race at Watkins Glen, in 1980. After winning the SCCA Super Vee title in 1982 and collecting the Rookie of the Year award for doing so, Andretti made his IndyCar debut in 1984 at Las Vegas. Although he was forced to share IndyCar's Rookie of the Year title with another up-and-comer, Roberto Guerrero, Andretti did more than enough to prove to everyone that he would be following in the footsteps of his famous father, Mario. In his rookie year Andretti scored nine Top Ten finishes, including five third places.

It took another year before the younger Andretti won his first IndyCar event, at the 1986 Long Beach (California) Grand Prix, but he sustained his momentum to finish second in the year-long points chase. In 1987 Andretti again was the series runner-up and, at the end of 1988, announced he would be joining his father at the Newman-Haas outfit. The pairing was a match made in heaven, with Michael

the younger Andretti scoring his third series runner-up finish in 1990, before dominating the 1991 championship and winning his first IndyCar series title.

At many races in 1994 Andretti, along with Nigel Mansell and Robby Gordon, posed the only realistic threat to the Penske team. Andretti proved that his Surfers Paradise victory was no fluke by driving the still-new Reynard to yet another victory, this one at Toronto, and

scored a further five fifth-place finishes during the year.

Before the end of the season Andretti had already finalized his plans for 1995. He would replace his father, Mario, at the wheel of one of the Newman/Haas Lolas.

ABOVE **Before joining Chip Ganassi's team in 1994, Michael Andretti drove for the McLaren Formula 1 team in 1993 and with his father for Newman-Haas in 1992.**

'NIGEL MANSELL'S WORST

NIGHTMARE

HAD COME TRUE'

DRIVER PROFILE

STEFAN JOHANSSON

Given a break here and there, Stefan Johansson could have been, indeed, should have been one of Formula 1's resident superstars. However, the FIA series' loss is IndyCar's gain, and the personable Swede has established himself as a firm favourite with the fans since his debut on the tour in 1992.

Johansson's credentials are impressive to say the least. After winning the 1980 British Formula 3 championship, Johansson contested the Formula 2 series the following year for Toleman (which later became Benneton), then for the fledgling Spirit-Honda Formula 2 team in 1982.

When Spirit-Honda entered Formula 1 in 1983, the team took Johansson with them, and the Swedish driver's best result was a seventh-place finish at the Austrian Grand Prix. That same year Johansson began driving the

ABOVE **Although he has yet to score a victory in IndyCar racing by mid-1994, Sweden's Stefan Johansson remains one of the sport's more accomplished racers.**

exotic FIA Group C entries, thus adding to his already undeniable experience.

In fact, it was in Group C that Johansson would claim his only FIA world title. Driving a Porsche with co-driver Bob Wolleck, Johansson won the 1984 world championship. On

his way to that title, Johansson still found the time to drive the cars he loved – the open-wheel Formula 1 machines – and during the hectic season he drove for Toleman and Tyrell, finishing second in the Japanese Formula 2 series.

Johansson's big break appeared to come in 1987 when he joined the McLaren team, but the season was not the success he and many others had hoped, and the following year Johansson was driving for Ligier.

Although his Formula 1 successes were few and far between, Johansson was still a hot property among the Group C teams, driving for Mercedes in 1988 and for Mazda in 1990.

Johansson's Formula 1 career effectively ground to a halt after the 1991 season, which he finished as the development driver for McLaren. Halfway through 1992, at the Detroit Grand Prix, Tony Bettenhausen

ABOVE **Here, Stefan Johansson is driving the team's spare car as shown by the X after the number.**

placed Johansson in one of his cars, and the rest, as the saying goes, is history. Johansson finished that race in third place and went on to win the year's Rookie of the Year award.During 1994 Johansson never made it to the victory podium, but came close on four separate occasions, scoring a fourth-place at Phoenix, and three fifth-places at Surfers Paradise, Cleveland, and Nazareth.

'HALFWAY THROUGH 1992 TONY BETTENHAUSEN PLACED JOHANSSON IN ONE OF HIS CARS, AND **THE REST IS HISTORY**'

TEAM PROFILE

PENSKE RACING

Although Penske Racing may not have won the PPG IndyCar series title in the first four years of the 1990s, there is no doubt that Roger Penske has the strongest, most resourceful team in the sport. At the time of writing Penske was running three cars in the series chase, driven by Emmerson Fittipaldi, Paul Tracy and Al Unser Jr. In the first three races of the 1994 season Fittipaldi and Unser Jr visited the winner's circle, at Phoenix and Long Beach respectively.

Penske, one of the most

ABOVE **It is possible that Roger Penske (left) is the most influential man in IndyCar racing. A consummate professional, Penske has many business interests outside IndyCars.**

powerful and influential men in motor sport, is a consummate businessman. In addition to running his racing team, he is founder and president of Penske Corporation (with business interests that include Detroit Diesel, Penske Truck Leasing, and car dealerships in

California). He is the major shareholder in Ilmor Engineering and owns Michigan International and Nazareth Speedways. In 1994 he announced a joint venture with Kaiser Steel Mills to build another speedway near Los Angeles.

Although to the outside world Penske appears to be just another successful businessman, he is a racer at heart. For a while he pursued his own driving career, qualifying for the 1961 and 1962 US Grand Prix, and when he retired from driving and turned his attention to running race teams, success came comparatively easily and he had victories in Can-Am sports car racing, Trans Am and NASCAR. He even dabbled in the politically charged arena of Formula 1, and, with Mark Donohoe driving, won the 1976 Austrian Grand Prix. In more than 30 years of racing, Penske Racing teams have been victorious in more than 80

events, including nine Indy 500 wins and eight IndyCar racing series titles. Penske still runs a NASCAR team with Rusty Wallace, one of the leading drivers on the tour.

When IndyCar racing was reorganized in late 1978, Penske was one of the founders of Championship Auto Racing Teams, Inc., which today is simply known as IndyCar.

Complementing the impressive driver line-up for 1994 are Chuck Sprague, the team manager; Nigel Bennett, the chief designer of the Penske race cars; and Rick Mears, a former off-road racer, who acts as team guru. Mears's involvement on the team is interesting. For years he was Penske's lead driver, but he suffered severe injuries while trying to qualify for the 1992 Indy 500. Mears recovered from his injuries but retired from active driving at the end of the season, since when he has devoted his energies to coaching Paul Tracy.

ABOVE **A mainstay of Penske Racing in the early-1990s has been former Formula 1 World Champion Emerson Fittipaldi.**

One final note on Penske. He loves nothing more than stealing the thunder of his rivals and on 13 April 1994 he did just that when, at Indianapolis Motor Speedway, he announced that for the 1994 Indy 500 his drivers would be using a Mercedes-Benz engine, built and designed by

RIGHT **Al Unser Jr went on to win the 1994 Indy 500 with a Mercedes-Benz, Ilmor engine.**

Ilmor Engineering, which is believed to deliver more than 900 horsepower. Although almost everyone knew that Mercedes-Benz would be getting involved in IndyCar racing, it was not expected until 1995. Once again, Roger Penske had got the jump on his competition.

Penske's gamble with the Mercedes at Indy paid off when Unser Jr scored a convincing win at the 500-mile classic.

After winning a stunning 12 out of 16 races in 1994 with his three-car team, Penske may revert back to a two-car system for 1995, with drivers like Unser and Fittipaldi. Penske retains an option on Tracy's services for 1995, but the young Canadian driver appeared headed for either the heady climes of Formula 1, or the vacant seat at Newman-Haas Racing, when the 1994 season finally drew to a close.

TEAM PROFILE

BUDWEISER KING

Although many observers point to Roger Penske as the best exemplar of a savvy businessman/racer, it could be argued that Kenny Bernstein is at least Penske's equal, and, unlike Penske, he still remains an active driver.

Bernstein's motor sports interests include not only his IndyCar team but also a competitive NASCAR team, headed by driver Brett Bodine, and an NHRA Top Fuel drag-racing team, which Bernstein himself heads. A four-time NHRA Funny Car national champion, Bernstein became the first drag-racing driver to exceed 300 mph (483 kph) in a piston-engined dragster when, on 20 March 1992, he recorded a 301.7 mph (485.4 kph) run at Gainesville Raceway in Gainesville, Florida. Outside of racing, Bernstein owns King Sports, Inc., a sports marketing

LEFT **This man knows what it is like to go really fast. IndyCar team owner Kenny Bernstein has gone more than 300 mph (483 kph) in his Top Fuel dragster.**

and public relations company.

Bernstein first fielded an IndyCar team in 1987 when, with driver Roberto Guerrero, the team entered the Indy 500 as Buick's official entry. The team continued to field Buick-powered Lolas until 1992 and at the Indy 500 in that year Guerrero drove one of the Quaker State oil-backed machines to a then-record 232.482 mph (374 kph) qualifying lap.

When the TrueSports team was disbanded in mid-1992, Bernstein lobbied hard for, and received, the team's Budweiser sponsorship, a perfect complement for Bernstein's dragster team, which is also backed by the Anheuser-Busch brand.

In 1993 the Budweiser King team contested the entire IndyCar series for the first time in its history, although success was hard to come by and Guerrero was released from his contract before the end of the season. Eddie Cheever replaced Guerrero for the final few races of the year, and the team was completely reorganized for 1994. Canadian Scott Goodyear joined from Walker Motorsports to be the Budweiser King's sole driver,

while David Benbow, who had formerly worked for both Tom Walkinshaw and Rick Galles, was appointed chief engineer. Frustrated at the team's apparent lack of performance and subsequent lack of results, midway through 1994 Bernstein announced he would leave the IndyCar series in 1995 and concentrate on his own thriving drag-racing career, and his successful NASCAR programme, headed by sprint car champion Steve Kinser. Ironically, just after the announcement, Scott Goodyear inherited an admittedly lucky win for the team at Michigan, its first and only success of the year.

ABOVE **Scott Goodyear heads the Budweiser King team's effort in 1994, although results in the first part of the season were not as spectacular as hoped for.**

TEAM PROFILE

RAHAL-HOGAN TEAM MILLER

Perhaps the most intriguing aspect of the Rahal-Hogan Team Miller outfit is that, in 1994, both lead driver and team co-owner Bobby Rahal, and second driver Mike Groff used Honda engines in their Lola chassis.

Many rival IndyCar teams feared the arrival of the Japanese engine manufacturer, anticipating that Honda would dominate the North American series in much the way it had done in Formula 1 in the late 1980s and early 1990s. Groff began testing the Honda engine in late 1993, and in 1994 both drivers used the experimental powerplant in competition, although early season results were not terribly encouraging.

Carl Hogan, a trucking magnate from St Louis, Missouri, quit motor racing in 1979 to concentrate on business. However, he joined forces with

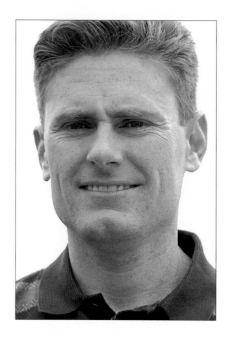

ABOVE **Mike Groff logged most of the test miles while the team got used to the unique Honda engine.**

Rahal to purchase the assets of Patrick Racing at the end of 1991 when Alfa-Romeo dropped out of racing. It proved to be a productive joint venture from the start, winning four races and the PPG IndyCar series championship in 1992.

Winning the championship made Rahal the first owner-

driver since A. J. Foyt in 1979 to win the IndyCar series title. For Hogan, whose previous experience as team owner included winning Formula 5000 titles with John Cannon in 1970 and David Hobbs in 1971, it marked his first IndyCar championship.

Buoyed by its early success, the Rahal-Hogan team began the 1993 season with a chassis of its own design, however, following a shock DNQ (Did Not Qualify) at the Indy 500 – which Rahal handled with creditable aplomb – the team reverted to the tried and tested Lola chassis, finishing the year in fourth place in the end-of-season points table.

Rahal commands fierce loyalty from his crew, and this is exemplified by the team's manager, Jim Prescott, who has been with Rahal for many years, including stints with the TrueSports and Galles-Kraco teams.

The team's alliance with Honda will extend no further than the end of the 1994 season. After a string of disappointing races with the Japanese cars, two-thirds of the way through the season the team announced it would be using the Ilmor-built Mercedes-designed units in 1995.

In another shake-up, the talented Raul Boesel was lured away from Dick Simon's team and will partner team-leader Rahal in the 1995 campaign.

ABOVE **The Rahal-Hogan team is typical of the teams racing IndyCars: two complete racing cars, between six and ten engines, tyres, equipment and many crew members.**

LEFT **Trucking magnate Carl Hogan, quit motor racing in 1979 only to return a dozen years later as a championship-winning car owner.**

TEAM PROFILE

GALLES RACING INTERNATIONAL

Rick Galles, owner of Galles Racing International, has won championships in every major motor racing series he has entered, including Super Vee, Can-Am and IndyCar.

Galles was introduced to motor racing as a sponsor on Al Unser Jr's dirt-track sprint car in the late 1970s, and from that time the two have enjoyed a successful, albeit sometimes bumpy, partnership.

Galles Racing International, which is based in Albuquerque, New Mexico, made its IndyCar debut in 1983, and by the end of 1993 it had recorded 19 series victories, won the 1990 IndyCar championship and won the 1992 Indy 500, the last two with Al Unser Jr at the wheel.

Recognizing that the teams that were doing most of the winning, Penske and Newman-Haas, were successful because they had developed their own

chassis, Galles attempted to develop his own chassis in the early 1990s. Designed by engineer Alan Mertens, the Galmer promised much, but it ultimately delivered just one major victory – the 1992 Indy 500. Despite the victory, the chassis programme was abandoned at the end of 1992. To make things worse, team-mates Unser Jr and Danny Sullivan feuded openly at race tracks across the country throughout 1993. At the end of the season Unser Jr left to drive for Roger

ABOVE **Rick Galles helped to bring Al Unser Jr to IndyCar prominence in the early 1980s. Galles now hopes to do the same for Adrian Fernandez.**

Penske, while Sullivan was released from the team.

For the 1994 season Galles placed his faith in the promising Mexican driver Adrian Fernandez and the equally promising Reynard chassis, with

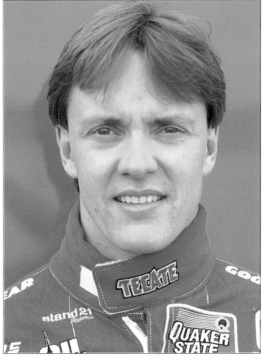

sponsorship support coming from Tecate beers and Quaker State oils. The team is managed by Ed Nathman, who had previously worked for Patrick Racing, McLaren North America and Newman-Haas.

Fernandez's driving credentials include Formula Ford victories in Britain and Formula Three competition in his native Mexico and in 1992 he competed on the Indy Lights tour.

ABOVE **Galles Racing International is one of several teams to use the new Reynard chassis in 1994.**

LEFT **Mexico's Adrian Fernandez carries Galles Racing's hopes in 1994. A former Formula Ford and Formula 3 driver, Fernandez graduated through the ranks of Indy Lights before joining the senior tour.**

113

TEAM PROFILE

A. J. FOYT ENTERPRISES

A J. Foyt Enterprises used to be the team name for one man: Foyt himself. The legendary driver from Houston, Texas, was essentially a one-man band and was somewhat sloppily organized, and this showed in race results, which, through the 1980s, generally ranked between poor and terrible.

However, since Foyt's accident in 1990 the team has matured, and in 1993 it enjoyed a successful season with young Robbie Gordon at the wheel of its primary car.

Foyt was upset when Gordon quit the team at the end of 1993 but then selected one of North America's most underrated drivers, Davy Jones, to head the team's efforts in 1994. Although he is probably a new name to followers of IndyCar racing, Jones's credentials are impressive. In the early 1980s he competed against such drivers as

ABOVE **Davy Jones was expected to head A.J. Foyt's racing team throughout 1994, but he was replaced by Indy Lights star Bryan Herta before the Indy 500.**

Ayrton Senna and Martin Brundle in the British Formula 3 series and spent six years with Tom Walkinshaw's sports car team, driving Jaguars in IMSA GTP competition. Jones also

performs well on the high-banked ovals of North America, where he often challenges the favoured NASCAR drivers at the wheels of full-bodied saloon cars in the International Race of Champions events.

Complementing Jones on the Foyt team is David Tennyson, who is scheduled to act as test driver for the outfit in 1994, while Foyt will field a car for his godson, John Andretti, in the Indy 500.

Heading Foyt's engineering staff is Bob Riley, who designed the Coyote chassis, which Foyt first drove at the 1971 Indy 500. The Coyotes are long gone, and Riley will be working with Ford-powered Lola chassis in 1994.

Jones only lasted three races with Foyt's team. After scoring a best finish of 12th at Phoenix, Jones was dropped prior to the Indy 500 in favour of 1993 Indy Lights series champion Bryan Herta. Herta quickly adapted to

ABOVE **Davy Jones headed A.J. Foyt Enterprises' racing effort at the beginning of the 1994 season, but he was gone by the time the field took the green flag for the Indy 500 in May of that year.**

RIGHT **Jonathan Byrd is affiliated to the A.J. Foyt team.**

the much faster Indy cars and, after finishing a very respectable ninth in the 500-mile classic, appeared set for a banner season until being seriously injured in a qualifying accident at Toronto.

With Herta on the disabled list for the remainder of the year, Foyt turned to another veteran driver, Eddie Cheever, who completed the season in steady, if unspectacular, fashion.

TEAM PROFILE

NEWMAN-HAAS RACING

The glamour team of IndyCar racing, if for no other reason than the presence of actor Paul Newman, must be Newman-Haas Racing. However, there is more to the team than just Newman. It has always boasted some of motor racing's best drivers, including over the years such Formula 1 luminaries as Jacky Ickx, Alan Jones, Peter Revson, Jackie Stewart and, of course, Mario Andretti and Nigel Mansell.

Carl Haas made his fortune by importing Lola chassis and Hewland transmissions into North America, and he has entered race cars in a variety of categories, although he did not compete in the IndyCar series until 1983. Newman arrived on the team in 1984, and the two have not looked back since.

Newman became interested in motor racing while he was making the movie *Winning* in 1968. Between filming commitments, Newman began

ABOVE **The flamboyance of Carl Haas (second from left) and the star-appeal of actor Paul Newman (right) have combined to make the Newman-Haas group the glamour team of IndyCar racing.**

driving in 1972, and he became an accomplished driver, winning two Trans Am saloon car races and four SCCA national championships.

The Newman-Haas team was one of the first to sign up with Ford-Cosworth when the British engine manufacturer re-entered IndyCar racing in 1992, and as a result, it has the first opportunity to try any engine improvements or modifications that Cosworth may try out. In addition, as the Lola importer to North America, the team serves as the "unofficial" Lola factory team.

The team is capably managed by Jim McGee, who has worked for many of the other high-profile teams in IndyCar racing, including Penske, Pat Patrick and Rahal-Hogan.

Perhaps the most unusual aspect of the team is its

sponsorship from the Kmart supermarket chain. The Kmart backing has enabled the Newman-Haas team to accumulate a wide variety of associate sponsors, including Dirt Devil, Gillette, BASF and Texaco/Havoline.

Entering the 1995 season the Newman-Haas team has something of a new look about it. Its two resident superstars of the past couple of years: Mario Andretti and Nigel Mansell have now departed. Andretti

announced his retirement from competitive IndyCar racing, while Mansell returned to the global stage of Formula 1. In their place came Mario's son, Michael, who last drove for the Newman-Haas team in 1992. Michael will replace his father at Newman-Haas in 1995 and Paul Tracy's name was mentioned as a likely replacement for Mansell's seat, but he is contractually tied to Roger Penske's outfit for 5 years.

ABOVE **Partnering Mario Andretti in the Newman-Haas team in 1993 and 1994 was Britain's Nigel Mansell. The extra lips on Mansell's helmet are designed to give improved aerodynamics.**

TEAM PROFILE

WALKER MOTORSPORTS

With Robby Gordon heading the driving line-up in 1994, Derrick Walker's team seems assured of success, a fact borne out by Gordon's impressive third-place finish at the 1994 Long Beach Grand Prix.

Joining Gordon in the three-car team in 1994 are Mark Smith and Willy T. Ribbs, who is sponsored by television personality Bill Cosby.

Walker, a Scotsman, is a relatively late arrival to the ranks of IndyCar owners. Formerly general manager of the Porsche IndyCar team and before that Roger Penske's vice president and general manager of racing, Walker became a team owner in 1991 when he acquired most of the assets of the disbanded Porsche outfit.

The team's best year to date came in 1992 when, after signing up Canadian Scott Goodyear and agreeing sponsorship with MacKenzie Financial, Goodyear finished second to Al Unser Jr at the Indy 500, posted a win at Michigan International Speedway and went on to finish an impressive fifth in the season's points table, despite competing on a very tight budget.

The team's sponsorship situation did not improve in

ABOVE **After helping Penske Racing to five Indy 500 and five PPG Cup titles, Derrick Walker decided to form his own team in 1992.**

1993, and after the excellent results of the year before, the season was disappointing.

Walker's fortunes changed in 1994, however. Gordon raced with a full sponsorship package from Valvoline, and the team also benefited from backing from Cummins (the world's largest diesel engine manufacturer), Craftsman Tools and Service Merchandise, a large department store chain.

Team engineer Tim Wardrop, who used to work for March Engineering, calls the tuning shots on a trio of Ford-Cosworth-powered Lola T94 chassis. Dick Caron, who previously headed Jack Roush's SCCA Trans Am team and worked for Dick Simon Racing, is team manager.

ABOVE **Walker Motorsports' 1994 effort was headed by young Robby Gordon, seen here at the Long Beach Grand Prix.**

TEAM PROFILE

DICK SIMON RACING

Dick Simon racing fields the team that is most likely to upset the established pace-setters, Newman-Haas and Penske.

Brazilian Raul Boesel heads the two-car team, with Japan's Hiro Matsushita driving the second car. Boesel is in his second stint with the team and, with sponsorship from Duracell Batteries, consistently keeps his Lola T94 near the front of the pack. In 1993 Boesel scored three second-place finishes and took the pole position at Milwaukee, underscoring his undoubted potential. The team runs a third car, co-owned by Frank Arciero, for another Brazilian driver, Marco Greco.

Dick Simon began racing in 1969, first with the fast Super Modifieds then, in 1970, with Indy cars. Simon's best finish as an IndyCar driver came during his first year when he achieved third place at the California 500.

LEFT **Before becoming a team owner together with his wife, Dianne, Dick Simon used to race Indy cars.**

After nearly 20 years in the fast lane, Simon quit driving in 1988 to concentrate on developing his race team.

Simon has been instrumental in developing the careers of several IndyCar drivers, in addition to Boesel and Matsushita. Simon played a significant role in Janet Guthrie's successful effort at the 1976 Indy 500, when she became the first woman to qualify for the 500-mile classic. Simon also assisted another woman driver, Lynn St James, in her IndyCar debut in 1992. St James finished 11th in the Indy 500 and earned Rookie of the Year honours for the race.

Former Formula 1 race car designer Morris Nunn heads Simon Racing's engineering staff.

ABOVE **Dick Simon**
Racing has fielded cars
for many promising
drivers, but perhaps
none has been more
talented than Raul
Boesel.

RIGHT **Dick Simon** has
played a significant
part in bringing new
drivers to IndyCar
racing, but the multi-
talented Raul Boesel
will probably be the
first of his drivers to
visit the winner's circle.

TEAM PROFILE

HALL RACING

For a team boasting such an impressive pedigree it is a little difficult to understand why Hall Racing, and its driver, Teo Fabi, are not regular visitors to the winner's circle. In fact, since being formed in 1991 the team has registered only one victory: at Surfers Paradise in Australia in 1991, and that was with John Andretti at the wheel.

Hall Racing began as the Hall/VDS Racing team. The VDS stood for Van de Stratten and engine builder Frank Weis; the Hall half of the equation for Jim Hall. (VDS Racing withdrew from the partnership at the end of the 1993 season.)

Hall's IndyCar racing credentials are impressive Throughout the 1960s and 1970s Hall was unquestionably one of the pioneers of the sport. While he was with the Chaparral Racing team, Hall introduced many items that are now taken

ABOVE **Jim Hall (right) is one of IndyCar racing's true pioneers, having helped to introduce such items as wings, plastic composites and automatic**

for granted – wings, plastic composites and automatic transmissions. In 1978 Hall helped driver Al Unser Sr to win three 500-mile races in one season: at Indianapolis, Pocono and Ontario (California). The

following year Hall was instrumental in the introduction of ground effects to IndyCar racing with his Pennzoil-sponsored Chaparral 2K. And in 1980 Hall helped Johnny Rutherford claim the Indy 500 victory and the IndyCar series championship.

After a ten-year sabbatical from the sport Hall returned to America's premier open-wheel series in 1991, with VDS and Andretti. After the initial win in Australia other successes have been few.

The team has run some of the best equipment, including, in 1994, a Reynard 94I chassis and Ilmor engines, and has one of the most underrated drivers in Teo Fabi, but Hall Racing has achieved only modest success in the early part of the 1990s.

After yet another season of moderate success, including a handful of top five finishes, Fabi, too, left at the end of 1994.

ABOVE **Italian Teo Fabi drives the only Hall Racing Reynard to be seen in IndyCar**

TEAM PROFILE

CHIP GANASSI RACING

LEFT **Chip Ganassi lured Michael Andretti back from Formula 1 to head his team for the 1994 IndyCar season.**

Chip Ganassi knows what it's like to win the Indy 500 and the IndyCar championship as a car owner: he did both in 1989, with Emerson Fittipaldi as his driver in a Penske-chassis entry, which he co-owned with Pat Patrick.

Before becoming a team owner in 1986, Ganassi was an accomplished driver who had competed in five Indy 500 races. Indeed, in 1982 Ganassi was the fastest rookie qualifier at Indianapolis Motor Speedway. However, after being involved in a near-fatal crash at Michigan International Speedway, his enthusiasm for driving waned and he concentrated on developing a race team.

When Fittipaldi left the Ganassi-Patrick team at the end of the 1989 season, taking his Marlboro sponsorship with him, the partners split up, Patrick forming Patrick Racing

International while Ganassi acquired the assets of the former organisation.

Ganassi persuaded the Target superstore chain to sponsor his team, and in a deal similar to Kmart's sponsorship of the Newman-Haas outfit, the Target backing gave Ganassi access to a variety of associate sponsors. Formula 1 refugee Eddie Cheever

drove for Ganassi in 1992 before being replaced by Arie Luyendyk in 1993. Although he has won no races, Luyendyk did qualify on the pole position for the Indy 500.

Midway through the 1993 season Ganassi announced that he would be running the then untried Reynard chassis in 1994. Then in September 1993, Ganassi

stunned the racing world by announcing that Michael Andretti, who was having a terrible time in Formula 1 with McLaren, would return to IndyCar racing as his driver for 1994. In what proved to be a prophetic move, Andretti drove the brand new Reynard to victory at the first race of the 1994 season at Surfers Paradise, Australia.

The team fields a second car, for Brazilian Mauricio Gugelmin, which is sponsored by Hollywood cigarettes.

ABOVE **After a disastrous few months in the world of Formula 1, Michael Andretti marked his return to IndyCar by driving Chip Ganassi's Reynard to victory in Australia.**

Aerodynamics The creative use of front and rear wings, the ground effects tunnel underneath the car, and a slippery body design combine to create the most effective aerodynamics package, which is essential for helping the cars travel around race tracks in the quickest possible time.

Balance When they are qualifying for a race, all drivers look for what is commonly termed the best "balance" for the car – that is, a combination of horsepower and a workable aerodynamics package. If the balance is right, the driver will not have to fight the car around the track; if it is wrong, the driver will be struggling to make the car complete the race.

Boost This is supplied by the turbocharger that is attached to the engine. On standard engines exhaust gases are released into the atmosphere. A turbocharger uses the same gases to power a compressor and to force compressed air into the engine. The extra air helps the fuel to burn better and produces more horsepower.

ABOVE **This is the trophy that all the drivers who compete at Indianapolis Motor Speedway covet – the Borg-Warner trophy, which bears the image of every winning driver of the 500-mile classic.**

Bumping This word is heard only around those drivers who are struggling to qualify for an IndyCar race. The actual field size is determined by such factors as the length of the track and pit accommodation, and if there are more cars than there are spaces on the starting grid, some drivers will not qualify. Bumping specifically refers to the driver who occupies the last qualified position for the race. Should another, non-qualified driver go faster, then he or she is "bumped" from the field and must make another (quicker) qualifying lap.

Championship Auto Racing Teams This was the previously unwieldy name for what now is known as IndyCar. When the car owners became unhappy with the way USAC was promoting IndyCar racing, they formed CART in 1978 to make the rules for IndyCar racing. A president (currently Andrew Craig) supervises the staff who administer the series. It's not an ideal way of doing business, but for IndyCar racing it appears to work with great success.

Drafting This is a technique that helps the cars to go faster. If one car is following immediately behind another, they will travel around the track faster because the car in front will create a hole in the air for the trailing car, while the trailing car will reduce air pressure on the rear of the leading car.

Ground effects *See* aerodynamics. A tunnel under the car creates a low-pressure area and effectively sucks the car down onto the race track.

Handling See balance. If a car handles well it means that the driver and crew have worked out the best combination of chassis set-up, suspension geometry, tyres and aerodynamics in the light of the prevailing weather to get the car around the track in the quickest possible time with the least amount of effort from the driver.

IndyCar *See* Championship Auto Racing Teams.

Methanol The fuel used by IndyCars, methanol is a high-octane fuel that requires less oxygen to burn than petrol. When it catches fire there are no visible flames.

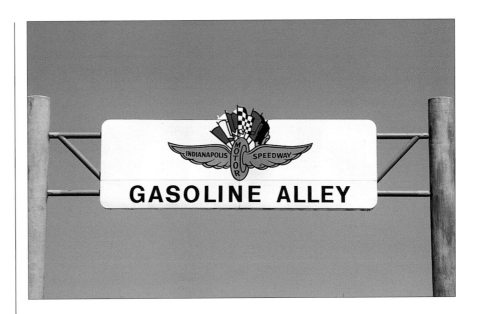

Oversteer This word applies when a car's rear end tries to push past its front end, particularly through corners.

Pit stop IndyCar races are won and lost in the pits. Assuming there are no on-track incidents, Indy cars have to come into the pits at regular intervals to refill the fuel cell otherwise they would run out of fuel before the race was completed. While in the pits, the crew will also change the tyres and make any aerodynamic adjustments deemed necessary – all in little more than 10 seconds.

Stop-and-go If a driver has transgressed some rule or another, he or she must return to the pits, stop for a moment, and only then rejoin the race.

ABOVE **Only 13 FIA Formula 1 World Champions have driven under the Gasoline Alley sign before competing in one of motor sport's greatest races.**

Understeer The opposite of oversteer. It applies when a car does not want to turn into a corner and would prefer to keep travelling in a straight line.

USAC The United States Auto Club, which governs most motor racing in North America. Although the IndyCar team owners fell out with USAC in 1978, they still go back to USAC's – and their premier race, the Indianapolis 500.

INDEX

*All illustrations are referred to
in italics.*